GW00392658

LADY ADDLE REMEMBERS

LADY ADDLE

From a Painting

LADY ADDLE REMEMBERS

BEING THE MEMOIRS OF
THE LADY ADDLE OF EIGG

Edited by
MARY DUNN

'The white flower of a blameless Wife'
Tennyson

ROBIN CLARK
LONDON

Published by Robin Clark Limited 1983
A member of the Namara Group
27 Goodge Street, London W1P 1FD

Reprinted 1983

First published in Great Britain by
Methuen & Co. Ltd., London 1936

British Library Cataloguing in Publication Data

Dunn, Mary
Lady Addle Remembers
I. Title
828'.91407 PR6054.U/

ISBN 0-86072-070-5

Printed and bound in Great Britain
by Mackays of Chatham Limited, Kent

CONTENTS

ILLUSTRATIONS

ILLUSTRATIONS

FOREWORD

WHEN I was first asked to publish my reminiscences, I hesitated for a long time, because I knew it would involve certain disclosures about some of the most illustrious names in Europe, including intimate details of my own family life. Destiny—that strange, wayward force that controls us all—has decreed that my ways should lie in high places. I have played halma with the great Lord Salisbury, I have bicycled with Bismarck, I have knitted a comforter for a King. It is not fitting, I argued, to speak of such moments.

But I was pressed to do so by many of my friends, including several whose names are household words in the literary world. Then came an offer from a publisher, which made me see things in a new light. I began to realize that it was a duty I owed to England— a sacred duty indeed—to pass on some of the rich inheritance of memory that is mine. And so here is my book—for England.

I have divided my little volume into phases wherein I have tried to find a resemblance in the landmarks of Life which have gone to make my character, to the development of a rose—for are we not all plants under the hand of that Great Gardener—Fate ?

I am particularly indebted to the Society for the Preservation of Ancient Relics for permission to reproduce some of the photographs included in the book, to the Athenaeum Club for remembering many of the names that I had forgotten, and, above all, to my dear father and mother, now long dead, without whose co-operation I should never have been in a position to write this book at all.

Blanche Addle of Eigg

PHASE I : THE BUD

CHAPTER I

CHILDHOOD

How dear to this heart are the scenes of my childhood
When fond recollection presents them to view.
Samuel Woodworth: ' *The Old Oaken Bucket.*'

CHILDHOOD at Coots Balder! What memories it
brings back to one! The fine old grey building with
its stately towers—its Gothic brewhouse—its Restora-
tion still-room, and its bathrooms built in what I still
hold to be the best and purest era of plumbing—the
late 'eighties. Nowadays people calling themselves
' decorators ' design bathrooms of black looking glass
and chromium plate. But to my mind there is nothing
to touch our old tiles of cabbage green, with the
mahogany bath tops worn almost white by the
splashings of many noble visitors . . . polished, one
might say, by the seats of the mighty.

Then the gardens, with their smooth green lawns,
their picturesque, sloping tennis courts and splendid
clock golf courses. Ah, what spacious days those
were! The interior of the house was just as fine, from
the state bedroom containing the magnificent bed, slept
in by two emperors, with four carved legs and fringed
pelmets, down to the vast pantry with its marble floor.

1

I happen particularly to remember that marble floor because it was the cause of a charming incident. One of the footmen—I think his name was Giles—had slipped on it and broken his leg, which necessitated his being removed to hospital just when we had a house party, which was most inconvenient for my mother. Nevertheless, with all her usual graciousness and consideration she went *the very next month* to the cottage where his mother lived to inquire after the boy. Dear old Mrs. Hummick was a great friend of ours and would never let us pass her door without begging us to come in and take a cup of nettle tea or a glass of gherkin wine. On this occasion she had an extra little present of a jar of tadpole jelly—a delicious recipe of her own—and when my dear mother thanked her (she had the most beautiful manners of any woman I have ever known and almost invariably thanked for any present she was given) Mrs. Hummick curtsied and said : ' You're very welcome, m'lady, and as for the boy's leg, he couldn't have broken it in a better house.' I always think that remark epitomizes the perfect relationship existing between employer and employée in the last century.

But I am going too fast, and must pause to say something about my family. My father was the thirteenth Earl Coot. He often said, with his usual delightful sense of humour, that he hoped it wouldn't bring him bad luck. Ours is a fine old family with many records of gallantry and daring. The seventh Earl was killed

MY FATHER, THE 13th EARL COOT

in a duel fought for the honour of Catherine the Great
—we Coots were ever the champions of lost causes—
while a great-uncle distinguished himself splendidly at
Waterloo, by fighting his way through a phalanx of
travellers and reaching the booking-office first—an
engagement in which he unfortunately lost a right
sleeve. Another ancestor died in the most unhappy
way. He was a great traveller and on returning from
the East one day brought back with him to Coots
Balder a young elephant, with the idea of using it to
carry him to and from church, though there is no
record of his ever having done so. But he became very
attached to the animal and insisted on making a pet of
it, even bringing it into the dining-room after dinner
and encouraging it to drink port. He was rather a
heavy drinker himself, I believe. One night, however,
he did not come up to bed as usual after his customary
two bottles and on going to the dining-room the butler
found the elephant fast asleep, kneeling on his unfortunate master, who was discovered to be dead. Pre-
sumably the unaccustomed weight had been too much
for him. Our dining-room is still said to be haunted
by trumpeting and the sight of an elephant's trunk
waving over the sideboard, and my father has more than
once, if he has stayed alone rather later than usual after
dinner, confessed to having seen and heard these
phenomena. No one else has ever had that experience,
but my mother, who is somewhat superstitious, has
always refused to preside over white elephant stalls in

3

charitable organizations, in deference to the family legend.

My mother was, before her marriage, Lady Arabella Twynge, daughter of the fifth Duke of Droitwich, and was considered one of the most beautiful women of her day. She had a faultless complexion, which she kept fresh and shining simply by the use of saddle-soap—no beauty preparations for her ! Her figure too was wonderful. Even to the last any of our horses' collars would go easily round her waist. I remember hearing M. le Pinceau, the celebrated French animal painter, remarking to a visitor on seeing my dear mother descend the staircase for dinner : ' Ah, what classic proportion ! Twice round her neck, once round her arm. Twice round her arm, once round her waist. Twice round her waist, once round the park. That is the rule I always use in painting cattle.' She was also the possessor of a very beautiful voice and one of my earliest recollections is of stealing down to the drawing-room one night and listening outside the door while my mother sang ' O Sole Mio ' with scarcely a note out of tune. After the song there was a pause and then Mr. Gladstone's voice said : ' Thank you, Lady Coot. That was kind of you.' Just those few words, no more. It shows how deeply he must have been moved.

I was the fourth to be born in a family of six, and the following day, the meet being at Coots Balder, I'm told I was held up in the drive for hounds to see me. How delighted my father was when one of them—Old

Roguie, I think it was—started mistaking me for a fox. ' She's got the right blood in her, bless her,' he said proudly, and so I had. Even now at sixty-seven I still drive as straight to hounds as my Rolls-Royce will permit.

I believe I was a particularly intelligent and lively baby and showed my great love of beauty at the very early age of four days, by swallowing one of my mother's pearl ear-rings. I was none the worse for that little adventure though and eventually the ear-ring was restored to Mama who declared that it would always have a special meaning for her ever after. Never, I think, was such a perfect mother, not one by whom the possession of children was more treasured. I could recount a thousand examples of her self-sacrificing devotion. As for instance, when she snatched my elder sister Soppy[1] up in her arms, at great peril to herself, just *one minute* before my grandfather's bathchair came round a bend in the yew walk. Or when we had scarlet fever and she insisted on our nannie remaining with us night and day for a week, without a second's relaxing of her vigilance.

I can see her now, her sweet face reflecting in its polished surface the flickering light of the night-nursery fire, as she bent over our beds and sang us to sleep with hymns and slumber-songs. After a verse or two we would invariably drop off and I have often noticed that her voice had the same soothing effect on others that

[1] Lady Sophia Coot, now Lady Hogshead.

5

heard her. Amongst other talents she had a great natural gift for poetry—I give one of her beautiful little poems at the end of this chapter—and also excelled in the art of letter-writing—an art long since dead, I am afraid. When it became known that I was writing this little book many of her old friends from all over the world sent me letters of hers which they had treasured for their charm and originality of style, and I now reprint one of the most delightful, lent by our old friend Connie Umbrage,[1] because it also shows the tremendous, almost passionate, love of nature which was part of her whole being.

' Coots Balder.   June 15th 1879.

' DEAR LADY UMBRAGE,

     ' I am so sorry I did not write to you yesterday as I intended, but I was prevented from doing so and therefore am writing to-day instead.

' We are much looking forward to your visit to luncheon on June the twenty-third and I hope so much the weather will be fine so that we can walk in the garden, which is looking very pretty just now as so many of the flowers are in bloom. Fine weather makes such a difference to a summer visit, I always think, as if it is wet one is confined to the house. In winter I do not think that it is such a disadvantage but with the arrival of summer it is a great disappointment not to be able to take the air, especially during the present

---

[1] Countess of Umbrage.

6

month when so many of the flowers are at their best.

' The weather has been sadly inclement lately but I greatly hope it will improve by June the twenty-third when we are much looking forward to seeing you.

'With kindest regards,

'I am Yrs. sincerely,

'ARABELLA COOT.'

Ah, those were the days when a letter from some one with a fine and noble mind was ' a thing of beauty and a joy for ever'.

AN ODE BY MY MOTHER

I give below the little poem which my dear mother wrote on the birth of her eldest child, my brother Crainy.[1]

> Only a bundle of muslin fine,
>   Only a swansdown hood,
> But Heaven has made that baby mine,
>   And that is what is good.
>
> Only a cot-ful of tears and joy,
>   Only a goffered frill,
> But the angels made him a baby boy,
>   And that is better still.
>
> Only a tiny wayward curl,
>   Only a crochet shawl,
> But Father has made him a future Earl,
>   And that is best of all.

[1] Viscount Crainiham.

MY BEAUTIFUL MOTHER

CHAPTER II

EARLY DAYS

I love it, I love it, and who shall dare
To chide me for loving that old armchair?
Eliza Cook : ' The Old Armchair.'

WE were a happy and devoted family, high spirited and
full of fun and yet with deeper feelings underneath and
acutely sensitive.   I shall never forget how my younger
brother Humpo[1] cried when he had pushed a small
cousin, who had come to stay, into the lake, and we
found out two days later that she couldn't swim.   He
was inconsolable and it was some time before my dear
mother could convince him that he wasn't naughty,
only ignorant, and wouldn't be punished for his
mistake.

We lived a healthy and homely life, with our games
and lessons, riding and picnics, almost as though we
were just like other children.   My father was a man of
great simplicity of tastes and would often accompany
us on one of the latter, choosing the spot himself in the
morning, with the aid of an estate map and his agent;
then later on our dear old butler, Turbot, with one or
two footmen at the most, would take the lunch and set

[1] The Hon. Humphrey Coot.

9

it out, seeing first that the chosen spot was thoroughly clean as Mama had a horror of dirt and even when she went to call on neighbouring houses always took a little rug to sit on, unless she knew exactly where the chairs had come from. This delicate fastidiousness she inherited from my grandmother, the Duchess of Droitwich, whom I scarcely remember—she died when I was six—but who, I am told, always wore white kid gloves in the house because of a rooted aversion from touching anything that had been fingered by the servants. She only removed them when she wanted to touch her husband or children. One morning, however, she absent-mindedly walked into his dressing-room while he was getting up and found that he was being dressed by the butler, and thereafter she wore gloves even when alone with the Duke.

Speaking of my grandmother reminds me of a most curious story connected with her death. My mother was very deeply attached to her, so much so that a quite unusual bond of sympathy existed between them which probably accounts for the episode. One night, she woke up in the greatest distress and told my father that she could see her mother on board ship, in peril of her life. She could not rest next day until she had sent down a courier to Brighton, where Grandmama was staying, to ascertain the state of her health. She was enormously relieved when he returned saying that my grandmother was perfectly well, and had not been on the sea at all, though oddly enough she had *considered* going for a row in a hired boat the previous week but decided that it was too cold. She did not die for two years, and then she was staying in Warwickshire, which is nowhere near the sea. The curious thing is that my mother did not dream of her that time at all. These things are certainly very hard to explain.

But to return to our childhood, from which I have somewhat digressed, what games we used to play! Hide-and-seek all over the house with 'home' by the stuffed rhino in the hall, shot by papa (who was a crack shot and on this occasion had taken a right and left at the beast and got him dead through the tail). 'Here we go round the Marchioness'—luckily there was practically always a Marchioness staying in the house to play it with—and 'Hunt the Coronet' which we were allowed to play on Sundays only, as a special treat! Our favourite place to hide it was on our governess's head. No one ever noticed her, so it was very difficult to find.

Then for more serious games there was cricket for the boys—my elder brother Crainy was very good indeed, and later on was in the village eleven and even once played for Leander Club—and for us girls, archery. My sister Mipsie[1] was the star performer and I well remember her taking aim at a black tree stump one day, about a hundred and fifty yards off, and hitting

---

[1] Lady Millicent Coot, afterwards Duchess of Brisket, later Lady Millicent Standing, then Princess Fédor Ubetzkoi and lastly Lady Millicent Block.

the bull's-eye which turned out to be our old vicar walking across the park to tea. But he took it all in good part and readily forgave any little discomfort he must have felt. Indeed, people did forgive Mipsie everything—she was so dazzlingly lovely and so audaciously mischievous. Later on, when her marriage to Oxo Brisket[1] turned out a failure people said hard things of her. But to me it seems as if she was just made for sunshine and enjoyment and luxury. To expect her to live, all except a bare three months in London for the season and August in Baden-Baden, in a grim old castle in Northumberland with nothing to look forward to but six weeks on the Riviera in the winter and a paltry month in Paris at Easter was little short of cruel to any one of her disposition. But Oxo was always very insensitive.

My father was a bit of a martinet and insisted on our being educated. We had, besides our English governess, a French Mademoiselle for French, a German Fraülein for German, an Italian Signora for Italian, a Spanish Señorita for Spanish, and a Russian Lady who took the dogs out. Our favourite was the Señorita, who was very pretty with flashing, dark eyes and a lovely figure. My father was particularly keen on our learning Spanish and often used to come into the schoolroom while she was giving us our lessons, so as to see how we were getting on. She left very suddenly, I never knew why.

[1] The Duke of Brisket.

MYSELF WITH SOPPY AND MIPSIE, 1873

Besides languages we were thoroughly instructed in music, art and dancing. My eldest sister Soppy inherited my mother's lovely voice and was much in demand at parties. I shall never forget her rendering ' The Lost Chord ' at a drawing-room concert in 1890. (Charity entertainments were only just coming in then, but Soppy was always very go-ahead and reckless and ' Hog', whom she had just married, let her do everything she wanted.) The concert was in aid of the R.S.P.C.A., and Soppy had cleverly altered the words to fit the occasion and had renamed the song ' The Lost Dog', which was a touching and beautiful idea, and I am not exaggerating when I say that I looked round afterwards and there was not a dry eye in the room. Some were wiping their eyes unashamedly and more than one pair of shoulders were shaking.

My second sister Maudie,[1] was really a great artist. Some of her water-colours still hang in the morning-room at Coots Balder and mama would often make visitors guess which were Maudie's and which were Constable's. Dear Maudie had a very distinctive style and they usually guessed right.

As for myself, well, my father used laughingly to call me Jack-of-all-trades. I have loved music all my life, and though not a real musician like Soppy, was considered rather an accomplished *siffleuse*, and I find in my diary that I have actually whistled in 118 village halls, 62 drawing-rooms, and 15

[1] Lady Maud Coot, killed out otter-hunting, 1896.

marquees during my life. Not such a bad record! I was always fond of painting and made quite a study of doily painting and illuminated menu cards when I was a girl. I loved to design suitable ones for all my friends—heather for Scotch people and wedding bells for wedding presents and all sorts of rather original little ideas like that. I think too they were appreciated because when I once asked a friend why I never saw hers put out (she was very fond of bathing and I had done her a lovely set with sharks on them) she said it was because she valued them too much to use them, which was delightful of her, I thought.

But the real passion of my life has been dancing. In my childhood I am told I would dance barefoot on the nursery Aubusson till my dear old nannie told me to stop, and later on in life I have taken the greatest interest in the Country and Morris Dance revival throughout England and am myself the president of the Society of Joyous Movement. It has always seemed to me the natural interpretation of happiness and enjoyment in this dear land of ours that we should express it with our limbs. Apropos of this I cannot help recounting an amusing incident which happened when I was putting my views very strongly to a certain bishop whom it would be indiscreet to mention. I was at that time very keen on a new movement to encourage folk dancing amongst the clergy and had myself invented a special dance called ' Curate on the Cob '.

I was urging the bishop to join it when with a twinkle in his eye he suddenly said : ' Can you see me dancing, Lady Addle ? I'm too portly.' Like a flash I answered : ' Portly is as portly does, m'lord.' Rather neat, I thought.

But my love of Terpsichore nearly cost me my life once. As I said before, I was very fond of dancing ' to myself' in the nursery, and I was indulging in this favourite pastime one day when suddenly I lost my balance and fell and *there was a bright fire blazing.* If it hadn't been for the high nursery fireguard I should undoubtedly have fallen into it and been severely if not fatally burnt. I remember saying to Nannie, who was in the room at the time and immediately left her ironing, dear faithful soul that she was, to pick me up : ' The angels took care of Blanchie, didn't they, Nannie ? ' ' Yes, my darling,' she answered, fondly consoling me with one of our home-grown pineapples : ' The angels must have put the fireguard there.'

A pretty and simple dance we often have at May Day festivities. Each man carries an empty champagne bottle and each lady an empty half-bottle.

(1) Set to partners. Advance six slips down and turn, tapping partner's shoulders with bottles.

(2) Up again back to places, bottles raised.

(3) Hands four and three slips down and across into the place of the fourth couple, who move up and round the second couple coming down again into the place where the first couple had been when the third couple were coming up.

(4) Repeat with shrill cries.

(5) The ladies advance three slips to the middle and form a ring, bottles outward. The men move round ten slips clockwise, ten slips anti-clockwise and kneel. Every lady then breaks her half-bottle on her partner's head.

This can also be danced with cider bottles for those who cannot manage champagne empties, but it is not nearly so picturesque.

CHAPTER III

F.OREIGN TRAVEL

Oh, to be in England !
Robert Browning.

MY father and mother were very broad-minded and were always determined that we should grow up knowing the world and realizing that there *were* things to appreciate in other countries. I have often felt grateful to them since, when my life has led me into all parts of the world, and I have found myself able to talk to foreigners almost as equals. Indeed, I have genuinely liked some of them, especially the Austrians, who are so like us, and the Norwegians—or do I mean the Swedes ?—with their fair English colouring. Even for America I have a respect. Is she not always seeking to emulate us and to possess our treasures of art and architecture, and does not that show that her heart is in the right place ? When my eldest brother, being utterly crippled by super-tax, was forced to sell the Tudor dovecote at Coots Balder, which was taken down stone by stone and perch by perch and shipped, together with a dozen of the famous Balder-pink fantails, to Cyrus Q. Haggett's lovely cottage in Pennsylvania, I comforted myself by thinking that our great loss was America's gain and that every one of those pigeons was an ambassador (or ambassador's wife) to that far-off land. It is that spirit, I am convinced, which is the keystone of the League of Nations.

But to return to youthful days, shall I ever forget how excited we were when mama broke to us that we were all ' going abroad ' for the first time ? In those times it was considered very unsafe to stay in Continental hotels as you never knew where the vegetables had been growing or what the foreign fish and meat had been feeding on when alive. So it was arranged that we should stay with relations who had married into foreign Royal families, so as to reduce the risk, at any rate in some degree.

Our first visit was to the Margraf and Margrafin Otto Von Bughaus at the historic schloss of Pestheim. The Margrafin was a second cousin of my mother's (she had been one of the Harrogate Twynges) and was the most gay and charming hostess imaginable. She had a very infectious laugh which would come bubbling forth on every occasion, whether humorous or otherwise, and which used to ring down the stone passages from end to end of the castle. Later on tragedy overtook her and the Duke turned against her and actually, I am told, bought a laughing jackass, which he said was the more intelligent pet of the two. After this inhuman cruelty she was forced to leave him and now she lives at Cheltenham with only a stone-deaf paid companion. It is very sad to think how little one nation really understands another.

But in those days what fun it all was! One felt one was living in one of *Grimm's Fairy Tales* and I used to lean out of my bedroom window and feel just like Rapunzel. My hair, at that age, came well below my shoulders and I could lie on it without much difficulty. Our young cousins, Hans, Heinrich and Elsa[1] were splendid companions, and both spoke English and played just like English children, so we soon entirely caught the atmosphere of German life and began to feel really almost cosmopolitan, though I should never have dared to use such a word in those days. Indeed, there was quite a little romance between Heinrich and me (I was sixteen and he was a year older), and when we left he gave me a pretty comfit box made out of a wild boar's back tooth which is in one of my spare rooms till this day.

From Pestheim we went, after some demur, to Italy. I say ' after some demur ' because my mother, who was a very strong Churchwoman, held the view that by going into a country which was a hotbed of Roman Catholicism one only encouraged it, but my father pooh-poohed that attitude—I remember him arguing that when my mother visited the workhouse it did not necessarily mean that she encouraged paupers, the truth of which she had to admit, so that to our great joy we soon found ourselves in the land of ice-cream and St. Francis of Perugia—of organ-grinders and old masters. And what happy memories

[1] Now Princess Stumpelbuffin-Blimpenheim-Warthog.

remain ! Seeing the Alhambra by moonlight, feeding the pigeons on the Bridge of Sighs, watching the gay Tarantula danced at Naples. I am proud to think I know that beautiful country so well from end to end.

An amusing incident took place at a lunch party in Rome at which dear old Cardinal Rondo was present. My brother Humpo, who was always rather an *enfant terrible*, and had never seen a priest's robes before, suddenly embarrassed us all by saying loudly : ' Mama, *who's that lady*? " There was one moment of horrified silence and then the whole table roared and the Cardinal himself patted my brother's head and told my mother that such a witty son should be a great social success—a prediction that has been fulfilled, for now he is grown-up Humpo is considered the joke of any party he attends.

We left Italy by way of Monte Carlo where papa had to stay on for business reasons which Mama said we were too young to understand. So the last lap of our journey was accomplished alone. This consisted of a visit to an old friend, the Duchesse de Concombre, who though not a relation was nevertheless of very noble birth, and was Concombre in her own right. What a real *grande dame* she was and what a stickler for etiquette too ! Even her horses were fed in order of precedence, according to pedigree, and on the anniversary of Marie Antoinette's death she would always evict a farmer on her estate in memory of the great Queen. But in her own home she was the soul of simple courtesy. She insisted for instance on any lady guest leaving the room in front of her. My mother had equally perfect manners and always refused to go out of a door before anyone of superior rank (a contretemps which very seldom occurred). This might have led to difficulties had it not been for my mother's lucky idea that during our stay only the rooms should be used which possessed double doors so that both could take their exit together, and this was accordingly done.

The Palais de Concombres is near St. Germain, so we were able to have many pleasant drives into Paris accompanied by the Madame's son, the young Prince de Carotte. It was during one of these excursions that the most extraordinary episode took place, which I have never to this day been able to understand.

The Prince was particularly anxious that we should see some of the picturesque Bohemian life of Paris as well as the *beau monde*, and this was readily consented to, with only the precaution of an extra footman. So one beautiful May afternoon we found ourselves driving down the *boulevardes* at Montmartre and gazing with interest at all the little cafés and the curious-looking people. Suddenly we discovered we were driving abreast of a handsome carriage and pair in which was seated a very beautiful lady with fair hair and a pale blue taffeta dress. Imagine our astonishment when we looked beyond her to her companion and saw that it was—Papa! Or rather someone so

21

like Papa that we simultaneously called out his name. We were still more surprised when the man, without paying the slightest attention to us, leant forward and said something to the coachman, who whipped up his horses and drove quickly on, turning eventually down a side street a little ahead of us. To add to the mystery, the young Prince, who had never seen Papa in his life, seemed so absolutely certain we were mistaken and dissuaded us from following him.

' But, monsieur,' I remember saying, ' I am positive it is Papa, because I recognize the check suit he is wearing. L'o let us go after him. He can't have recognized us.'

' *Vous vous trompez, mesdemoiselles,*' he said. ' *Il est impossible que cela soit M. votre pére. J'en suis certain.*'

He even persuaded us not to recount the incident when we got back to my mother and the Duchesse, so that to this day I have never been able to solve the mystery. Why was the Prince so convinced ? Had my father a double, or was he really in Paris that day, perhaps again on business? When we arrived home Papa had already returned from Monte Carlo and had such exquisite presents for us all that I'm afraid it put everything else out of our heads.

A GOOD REMEDY FOR SEA-SICKNESS

I reprint a letter which I wrote to *The Lady* some time after my first trip abroad, on the subject of sea voyages. It may prove of some use to other travellers afflicted with that dreadful scourge, *mal-de-mer*.

'DEAR LADY,

'I read with much sympathy and interest the letter from "Prostrate Victim" in your last week's issue. I have also suffered, as she has, from the miseries of the sea, not the least being the terrible way it has of making one lose all sense of being a lady and just not caring who sees you in a position of indignity. I would suggest that "Prostrate Victim" tries the following remedy for a *short voyage*, which was given me by a foreigner, but which, nevertheless, is quite safe and very efficacious, at least so I have found it.

'Take on board with you a few camphor balls (you need not declare them), ask for a jug of boiling water to which you add half a teaspoonful of brandy (this must seem sadly unwise advice to give a young lady, but I assure you it will do you no harm) and the yolk of one egg. A pinch of saffron will not come amiss for those who like the flavour. Pour all this into a basin over the camphor balls and wait till they have melted. Then empty the whole thing away. By that time you will have reached Calais and will have been so interested in what you were doing, that it will entirely have taken your mind off the sea. Of course, the strong smell of camphor or saffron may upset you, in which case it may make you a little sick, but nothing to speak of. I hope this will prove of service to " Prostrate Victim ".

' Yours truly,

' SUCCESSFUL SEA-NYMPH.'

CHAPTER IV

COMING OUT

But when a snowflake, brave and meek,
Lights on a rosy maiden's cheek,
It starts—' How warm and soft the day ! '
' 'Tis summer '—and it melts away.
  Mary Mapes Dodge : ' The Snowflake.'

I SUPPOSE the most important moment in a woman's life, next to the big things—marriage and religion and servants, is the moment when she stands, meta-phorically, on the threshold of womanhood, and actually on the threshold of the drawing-room, trying to summon up all her courage to enter for the first time *with her hair up*. Never shall I forget the agony of it as far as I was concerned. We had a dinner party that night, I remember, and I was put to sit between Lord Leighton, who was a great friend of our family, and a rising young politician who later became Prime Minister. I forget his name for the moment (we have, of course, known all the Premiers, so one gets confused). Hardly had we started dinner when I realized to my horror that something was slipping, and as I bent forward to make a remark to Lord Leighton a bronze hairpin slithered out of my hair and fell with a splash into his soup. An embarrassing situation for a young girl! But never shall I forget that great man's kindly action. He fished it out with a fork, dried it with the silk handkerchief which he always kept to polish his glasses and put it in his breast pocket, saying : ' Now, Lady Blanche, I have a keepsake that is worthy of you.' Afterwards he asked my mother if he might paint me as Godiva, but Mama said one never knew what those classical paintings involved, so his kind suggestion was refused.

The subject of hair reminds me of many amusing things that happened to my friends and family at that fatal time. My sister Maudie's hair came down in church one morning, and our dear old vicar—the one that Mipsie had wounded in the broad alley—had to wait till it was put up again as my mother's attention was occupied in helping her. Dotty Bush[1] had been given a wrinkle that a little glue brushed through the hair at night made it ' stay put ' in the morning. Unfortunately in her zeal she overdid it and was found by her maid stuck fast to the pillow next day! But the most amusing incident of all was when a very shy young cousin, Edith Twynge, came to stay when she was just out. In those days it was the fashion to do one's hair in big rolls from the front of the head to the back and under the rolls went little wads of hair—frizettes they were called. My brother Humpo,

---

[1] Lady Bush of Shepherd, *née* Bottlewell.

who was an incorrigible practical joker—he even showered his own hair with pepper at his wedding so that the service was held up while the dean[1] sneezed 107 times—had crept into her room and substituted a partially drugged mouse for one of the frizettes. Edith, who was a little short-sighted, never noticed the exchange and came down to breakfast as usual, where we all (being let into the secret) watched her with excitement. Suddenly the chloroform wore off and the mouse began to stir; Edith, thinking her hair was coming down, clutched her head and then screamed as the mouse jumped on to her shoulder and quickly disappeared in the lace at her neck, while we all—including my father—rocked with laughter, knowing how terrified Edie was of mice. Humpo always meant to try her on her next visit with a rat in her sponge-bag, but unfortunately she was taken ill with a bad nervous breakdown soon after leaving Coots Balder and she never came to stay again.

I actually came out at the Ladies' Ball at Brighton in 1885, though my father and mother gave a ball for me a few weeks later at home. My coming-out dress was simple and dainty in the extreme, being made entirely of quilted bombazine caught up over a heavy white ottoman with little bunches of roses carved out of rock crystal. My sister Soppy, who had been out two years, wore a pretty puce grenardine

---

[1] Humpo was the only one of our family not to be married by a bishop. The reason is explained later

27

festooned with ermine tails. We stayed with the Duke and Duchess of Portslade and were honoured to be in the same party as the Prince and Princess of Wales, afterwards King Edward and Queen Alexandra. The latter was as gracious and charming as ever and commented, I believe, favourably on my appearance, and when she was told who I was, asked to speak to me and was kind enough to tell me I should never be as beautiful as my mother. The same day after luncheon I picked up a skein of embroidery silk which she had dropped and she thanked me with a delightful smile and said : ' Surely you are Arabella Coot's daughter ? ' Another instance of her wonderful memory.

Besides myself, many important girls came out that season—most of them lovely too. There was beautiful Bee Vigo, Lord and Lady Conduit's girl, who afterwards married Lord St. Omach and then ran away with ' Masher ' Smith, who had to leave his wife in consequence. Lovely, frail Lily Busk with her white face and drooping ways, so like the flower she was named after. I remember her going to The Lancashire House Ball dressed simply as ' An Arum ' and looking so life-like in her purity that she was never asked for one dance throughout the evening. At the next ball she changed her style somewhat and went as a tiger lily and soon after that she married well and had, I believe, eleven children.

But the prettiest of all the pretty girls of that date,

my own family excepted, was dear vivacious, enchanting Dorothy Divott[1]—'Duckie' as she was always called, and what a duck she was! The life and soul of any party, always the leading spirit of dumb crambo— the daredevil in beggar-my-neighbour. She was as sweet and unselfish as she was lively too. When a game of lawn tennis was held up because the ball was lost in the St. John's Wort it was Ducky who would go on hands and knees, regardless of earwigs, to retrieve it. When Humpo used to play his most popular practical joke of ink in the claret it was invariably Ducky who would offer her own spare-room inkpot and help him to decant it. In these and a hundred other ways she made herself beloved by all, so that it is not to be wondered at that when my eldest brother Crainiham openly showed his admiration it was looked upon with nothing but favour from our parents.

I shall always remember their first meeting. Somehow I knew instinctively how it was with him from the start. Crainy was always rather quiet and reserved, though not from any lack of brains, because he passed fifty-first into Sandhurst after only two years at his crammers—this being a record in our family. But he very seldom spoke in sentences of more than one or at the most two words, and practically never expressed an opinion on anything at all. This was due not to any cowardice, but rather to a rare and splendid honesty which I know made

[1] Hon. Dorothy Divott, second daughter of Lord Foozle.

him hold—though I never, of course, actually heard him say so—that no man should express an opinion on any subject unless he previously had an opinion to express. Imagine our surprise, therefore, when on first being introduced to Ducky at a garden party, after barely ten minutes silence, we clearly heard Crainy say : ' It's a lovely day, isn't it, Miss Divott ? '

Well, anyone who could make Crainy sparkle like that was a genius and my romantic mind was made up on the spot. Crainy and Duckie should marry— nothing should stop it. Unless, I suddenly thought with horror, the rather exacting bridegroom's part of several sentences should prove too great a strain for him. But we'll take that fence when it comes, I decided, lapsing into a metaphor culled from my well-loved sport.

But, alas, how all our fondest plans are brought to naught ! Only too soon came the tragedy and scandal which horrified society, reverberated round Royalty itself, and shook my poor father from end to end.

FROM MY DIARY

The following may be of interest to youth as showing how we of the older generation spent our days. Sometimes the young people of to-day say there wasn't much excitement or event in our lives, but I think these extracts prove that, on the contrary, our time was very fully occupied with interesting and sometimes stirring things. I have selected just a typical week in the autumn of 1888, when I was nineteen years old.

Saturday, Sept. 29th. A fine day, rather cold. Mipsie and I did the church (Harvest Festival). Not enough fruit, so asked for more and Mrs. Chambers brought in eight more marrows, which was really too many. Put two more by the font, two by the lectern, and four propped up against the screen. They didn't look very well, somehow, but, after all, God created marrows so it must be all right to use them. Grandmama and Aunt Ethel came by the 3.45. Lawn tennis after tea. Aunt Ethel got rather vexed with Crainy because she said he tried to put the balls where she could not reach them. We assured her he didn't mean to and I think she understood, but it somewhat spoilt the game. After dinner papa, Aunt E., Crainy, and Soppy played whist. I got on with my Girls Friendly night-gowns. Had to unpick a whole sleeve. Decidedly tiresome day.

Sunday, Sept. 30*th*. Church. New vicar took service. Rather high, but nice. Papa says he is not a gentleman, which is very sad. Changed and took my Bible Class as usual. Had to send Mabel Bright out for hiding a banana. After tea painted texts for dear Mama's birthday. I did cornflowers, Soppy raspberries and currants, and Mipsie budgerigars.

Monday, Oct. 1*st*. (Pheasant shooting.) Busy day. Drove down to the village with Grandmama to visit. Poor old Kitney very bad with rheumatism, and worse since I last saw him and took him Mama's liniment. Changed for tea, and brushed Spot afterwards. Found a fl—— but asked Aunt E., who was watching, not to tell Papa. Sang glees after dinner till we woke Grandmama, then stopped.

Tuesday, Oct. 2*nd*. Drizzle. Rode in morning. The new vicar's wife came and asked us to help in a village concert on Nov. 2nd. Very Exciting. Consulted Soppy what I should whistle, as I've done ' Minstrel Boy ' fourteen times in Balder and they may know it. Soppy suggested she should sing ' They all loved Jack ' and I should whistle an obligato. What a lovely idea. Just like Patti and Joachim.

Wednesday, Oct. 3*rd*. Cold and dull. Papa came back from shooting very tired and said the pheasants

MYSELF AS 'INDIA' IN THE CHURCH PAGEANT
OF 1897

were no good this year. Aunt E. *told him about the fl——.* Papa very angry and says I don't know how to look after a dog. Cried in my room for a long time.

Thursday, Oct. 4th. Lovely warm day. Lady Umbrage and Hilda came to tea. A Mr. Thorpe, a friend of Crainy's called. He asked Mipsie to show him the grotto. Aunt E. heard him and told Mama, who told Papa, who was very angry and said Mr. Thorpe must never come again.

Friday, Oct. 5th. A lovely day. Saw Grandmama and Aunt Ethel off by 12.30 train. Changed into my blue, which I always like best for lunch. Wrote letters till tea-time. Then changed and went for a tricycle ride in the park with Soppy and finished off my text only just half an hour before dinner ! The new vicar and Mrs. Spurge dined to talk about the concert He is delightful and *seems* a gentleman, but papa says not. Conversation and music till 10.30. Not in bed till 11. What a day !

PHASE II : STORM AND SUNSHINE STRENGTHEN THE PLANT

CHAPTER V

TRAGEDY

Oh, call my brother back to me !
I cannot play alone.
The summer comes with flower and bee,
Where is my brother gone ?

Felicia Hemans : ' *A Child's First Grief.*'

IT is painful for me to write this chapter ; it will be
equally painful for the public to read. Even reading
the draft of it was enough to upset my husband to such
an extent that he suffered from insomnia at the club
for over a week. As for myself, it is not difficult to
imagine my feelings on the subject. To a mind still,
as it were, saddle-sore with memory, it is nothing
short of agony to touch on the old sensitive places.
But in a truthful autobiography it is impossible to
leave out an event of such importance to our family
and to Debrett itself. Also it seems only fair to put
before the public the alternative theory which I myself
hold to this day about the episode.

It was particularly unfortunate that it should have
occurred during one of the frequent visits of his Imperial
Majesty William II to Coots Balder, though I must
hasten to add that although he was actually taking
part in the fatal game of croquet, no reflection has ever

been made against his play, which was honourable to the last hoop. It was, alas, Crainy, and Crainy alone, on whom suspicion fell.

It had been an exceptionally gay and brilliant party, I remember. Humpo was at his funniest, while Soppy had been in splendid voice, and would have sung right through the arias of *Athalie* the first evening, had not the Kaiser, with considerate solicitude, begged her to desist for fear of overtiring herself. As for Mipsie and Dotty, they were the life and soul of the party, whether they were helping Humpo with his jokes—the naughty creatures smeared all the whist cards with treacle, and put an under-housemaid in every visitor's bed one night (what screams of laughter there were afterwards !) —or playfully threading dandelions in the Archbishop of York's beard—or playing charades, or quoits, or croquet with equal enthusiasm and grace.

As I write the word ' croquet ' a pang goes through me. If that wretched game had never been invented, to tempt men to recklessness and dishonour, Crainy might still be continuing a brilliant career in the army, married to the girl he undoubtedly loved, instead of— but I will tell the whole story.

It was on a radiant afternoon in July that the fatal game was played—Crainy and Dotty against the Kaiser and an aunt by marriage, Lady Brine and Spa, wife of my mother's brother.[1] Aunt Queenie had

[1] The Marquis of Brine and Spa, eldest son of the Duke of Droitwich.

36

never greatly liked Crainy. It was well known that she had sworn that nothing would induce her to forgive him for a childish misdeed—I would prefer not to say what—when he was staying with her at the age of four. It was therefore most unlucky that she should have been the only witness—and can we trust her account ?

It is difficult to tell exactly what happened. The Kaiser, apparently, had just played and had gently roqueted Crainy's ball, so that it was wired for the next hoop, which H.M. had afterwards gone through himself. It was then Crainy's turn to play. The Kaiser was sitting on a seat with Dotty, who in her winsome way was playing ' Tinker, Tailor ' with his buttons, much to the Royal delight. Suddenly they were startled by a scream, and looking up, they saw Aunt Queenie bearing down upon my brother with a face suffused with purple —a colour of which she was inordinately fond—while Crainy's ball was through the hoop and careering merrily along the other side. Then it happened— the cruel, the unbelievable, the malicious slander. Crainiham was accused of cheating.

I give their conversation exactly as it was told me later by Dotty, in between racking sobs.

' Crainy,' said my aunt, ' you cheated.'

Crainy did not say anything.

' Your ball was wired for that hoop and couldn't possibly have gone through,' she continued.

Crainy remained silent.

'Besides,' my aunt went on, 'with my own eyes I saw you move the red with your foot.'

Crainy did not speak.

At that poor Dotty burst into tears and left the lawn, crying: 'Oh, Lord Crainiham, how could you!'

Crainy did not reply.

The game, of course, was abandoned and my father and mother told immediately. All the guests very considerately left by the next train, and the blinds were drawn down. The family was alone with its sorrow. It was a terrible evening for us all. I had never seen my father so upset; indeed so ill was he that he left untouched two out of the seven courses at dinner, and refused a third glass of port, a thing I have only known him do on one other occasion, after the death of a favourite sheep. My mother was amazingly brave. Except for sobbing quietly all through dinner she gave no sign of what she must have been suffering. The rest of us talked in hushed whispers, and even Humpo was subdued, and after having tried in vain to cheer us up by putting pondweed in the spinach, gave it up and spent the evening biting his nails. Crainy, I couldn't help noticing, was particularly quiet.

I do not know what happened after dinner except that Papa had a long talk with my brother, in which he gave him, I believe, a chance to clear himself of this awful accusation. Nay, he implored him on what would have been bended knees, if his gout had not been unusually troublesome at the time, to do so, reminding him that we Coots are famous for our honour—there is an old saying that honour and hiccoughs are the hall-marks of a Coot—but all in vain. Crainy would not speak. The same night he sent in his papers and the following day he bid us all a silent farewell and sailed for Africa. I have before me as I write his first kill—a tsetse fly, stuffed and made into a paper-weight.

That is the story of our family tragedy as the world heard it. But there is also *my* theory of the episode, which, if only it could be proved, would for ever clear my brother's name of any suspicion. The whole problem seems to me to turn on the question of Crainy's silence. Was it because he could not think of anything to say, or was there some other reason ? I maintain that there was, and that it was this : It is well known that there were always a quantity of moles on the estate at Coots Balder—indeed our motto makes a playful reference to them[1]—so is it not possible that one of them, attempting an exit on to the croquet lawn, had projected his or her nose under Crainy's ball and given it the little push which my aunt declares she saw ? If that were the case, how it alters everything ! For I know my brother. I know how every plantain on the tennis court, every wasp in the pantry was as dear to him as his own mother. Nothing would have induced him to betray an estate mole—he would have died

[1] *Sic mole, sic molibus.*

39

first. So he kept silence. And the ruin of his career was the penalty of his loyalty, as is often the case.

But I am happy to think he has not been alone in his misfortunes. Ten years ago he married Miss Hermione Boodle, daughter of Sir Alfred Boodle, Bart., a good old family, and a dear girl, though she unluckily has a bad cast in one eye and has been a life-long sufferer from spots. A slight impediment in her speech makes her very shy and retiring, and they live, even now when Papa is dead, mostly at one of the family places near Troon, in Ayrshire. They have three attractive children, all the image of their mother. Crainy became very keen on golf and with his natural aptitude for games soon achieved a handicap of twenty-four. But lately, I hear, he has given it up, owing to some silly fuss at the club. There is no doubt about it that some of those Scotch courses are overrun with moles.

LAMENT FOR CRAINY

The poem which I wrote after the tragic happenings at Coots Balder described in the last chapter. Though I could never have the same inspired touch as my mother, it shows that I have inherited, so I am told, a little of her wonderful gift.

Thou art under a cloud, dear Crainy,
    Under a thick, dark cloud.
And thy parents grieve for thine honour,
    Thy sisters are weeping aloud.
Thou hast gone from their gaze so loving,
    In a far-off land to roam,
Where dangerous lions and poisonous flies
    Will make thee think of home.

We shall see thee again, dear Crainy,
    When the scandal has quite blown o'er ;
One day thou wilt come back sailing
    To England's blessed shore.
And the Balder bells will ring out
    And a Balder calf be slain ;
The Regiment will forgive thee,
    And thy clubs elect thee again.

I believe in thee still, dear Crainy,
  And thine honour's stainless steel.
I believe thou wert guided by motives
  That only a Coot can feel.
In a finer game than croquet
  Thou hast played an undying part,
When thou went'st through the hoop of loyalty
  With the ball of a noble heart.

CHAPTER VI

ENGAGEMENT

A flower when offered in the bud is no vain sacrifice.
                                              Isaac Watts.

It is a relief to turn from the bitter pages of the last chapter to a more happy event in my life—I refer to my marriage after a whirlwind courtship of only three years, to John Hector Murdoch Hirsute McClutch, seventeenth Baron Addle of Eigg, and one of the best and noblest men that ever wore a sporran.

Our first meeting makes quite a romantic story. After Crainy's sad departure we all felt we should never have the heart to roquet a ball again, and Mipsie and I took up bicycling instead, which was just then becoming all the rage. Dear papa bought us beautiful machines costing £30 each, and we had pretty blue frieze costumes which allowed plenty of play for one's lower limbs. We always wore skirts and the malicious rumour which was started in the village by the doctor's wife, that she had seen Mipsie coasting down the Chestnut Avenue in the park in mustard bloomers, is utterly untrue. And, anyway, what right had she to be in the park at all ? She was trespassing, and should never have mentioned anything she *did* happen to see.

For the first few weeks we kept exclusively to the park drives, but later on we became bolder, and used to go for quite long rides of two or three miles on the roads—only on our own property, of course—and in time became really proficient and did not even have to get off for carts.

It was while we were enjoying these delightful excursions that we several times noticed a very good-looking young man who evidently derived the same pleasure as ourselves from bicycle rides, though he always seemed to take his alone. Once, on getting off for a gig, I happened to look back and saw that he had also dismounted and was gazing in our direction.

Soon after this, Mipsie became engaged to Oxo Brisket and what with the excitement and social whirl of the wedding preparations our bicycles had to be laid aside. The wedding was the most brilliant event of the season, for Mipsie was a celebrated beauty, and Oxo one of the most eligible dukes of his day, with an immense fortune (he owned the whole of Smithfield meat market, and indeed gave his name to the famous joint) ; but afterwards, when it was all over and the rice swept up and given to the tenants for their rice puddings—a generous act of my mother's, so typical of her habitual thoughtfulness for the poor—how depressed we all felt ! I remember going to Mipsie's room and throwing myself on the bed in floods of tears to think she would never be the same again. I recalled the old days and the fun we had had with our lawn tennis and our bicycle rides. Now they were all over. Suddenly I sat up and pushed the tangled hair out of my eyes. A rather reckless idea had occurred to me. Why shouldn't I go for a bicycle ride by myself?

No sooner had I decided than the deed was done. In forty minutes I had changed my dress and within an hour and a half had got my bicycle out myself and was bowling merrily down the drive towards the front gates. There I should have stopped, of course, but girls will be girls, and I have always been attracted by any adventure with the element of risk. With a beating heart, and hoping fervently that the lodge-keeper wouldn't see me, I slipped out of the great gates and found myself outside, alone, on the open road.

What a wonderful sensation freedom is, and how I enjoyed pedalling briskly along between the perfectly trimmed Balder hedges, ringing my bell gaily at every bend! But my triumph was short-lived. Gradually I grew aware that the road was becoming increasingly bumpy and there was a peculiar noise at the back of my machine. I got off and looked. Alas, my back tyre was quite flat. I looked for the pump. *It was gone!*

It is in a crisis, they say, that blood tells. When I reflect now on the situation and realize—there I was, a young and delicately nurtured girl, alone and un-protected at least a mile and a half from home with no possible means of regaining its precincts, I am proud to think that I kept a stiff upper lip and never allowed myself to give way to panic. ' Be a Coot,' I remember saying to myself, as I quickly drew my machine on to the grass to save the tyre from further friction. My husband has since told me that it was my instinctive thought for my bicycle before myself that first drew him to me.

I had scarcely passed ten minutes in weighing the pros and cons of walking back on the road over which I had come, or walking on over the road ahead of me—both routes would have led me to Coots Balder in about the same time—when suddenly round the corner came a bicycle. It was a man's bicycle, and seated on it was—a man ! That man was my future husband.

Immediately he recognized me he sprang off his machine with a charming look of concern on his handsome face. I shall never forget his first words.

' I say, can I help you ? ' Then with a quickness of perception which I learnt later on to know and love : ' I see your back tyre is flat. Perhaps you have a puncture ? '

In a moment he had whisked out his own pump and was bending over my back wheel, while I watched admiringly the strong young shoulders and noted the ease with which he pumped the tyre up without once having to pause for breath. Then he straightened himself and felt the rubber with a master hand.

' I think that's all right now,' he said. ' It was just flat—not a puncture as far as I can see.'

46

Then came words that sent the hot blood coursing into my cheeks: 'We are both fond of bicycling, aren't we?'

What I answered I scarcely knew. I murmured some conventional reply in a whirl of embarrassment and happiness to think that he had remembered those other rides too, and the next thing that I knew was that he was gone. Only when he was round the corner and out of earshot, did I discover that he had left his pump behind.

There was never any doubt in my mind but that it was a deliberate act on his part and no accident. He wanted to leave me protected and safeguarded against any possible future deflation, while he deliberately exposed himself to the same risk. That was Addle all over.

Modern girls will laugh at me for being sentimental, but I am not ashamed to confess that for five nights running I slept with that pump under my pillow, and woke each day to find myself holding fast to the handle. We Victorians may be considered old-fashioned, but we had our glorious moments of real romance.

On the sixth morning I came down to breakfast a little late (because hiding my dear souvenir each day from prying eyes was no easy task) to hear Mama reading out a letter she had just received from Lady Addle, saying that her son was quartered quite near us with his regiment and asking Mama to invite him to Coots Balder. An invitation was sent down at once,

and that afternoon to my astonished delight my unknown friend arrived to play lawn tennis, and turned
out to be none other than the young Lord Addle.

Then followed months spent in a whirl of happiness,
as acquaintance ripened into friendship, and friendship
into something warmer. Addle had all the romantic
impetuosity of the Celt, and it was not many weeks
before he had asked me to partner him on the lawn
tennis court. There I was struck afresh by his unselfishness in calling out ' yours ' to any ball he was unable
to take, and his rigid sense of honesty, which forbade
him even once to say that his opponent's ball was out
when he knew that it was in. That, I decided, was
the husband for me.

And so the years sped on, and at last came the day
when Addle asked me to be his wife. Even that was
typical of his nobility of character. The occasion was
a ball at home, and we had danced twice together, I
remember, regardless of scandal. Afterwards he led
me to our magnificent conservatory, and seating me
gently between two fine red-hot pokers, sank on his
knees and told me that he loved me. It was a wonderful
moment and I was sorely tempted to say ' yes ' at
once. But I dared not allow myself to be swept off
my feet by the suddenness of it all, so I paused for ten
or twelve moments considering my answer. It was
then I noticed that his forehead was damp and his face
drawn as though in pain. That decided me. ' If he
really loves me like that,' I remember thinking, ' it must

come right.' I hesitated no longer, but gave him my hand, and I shall never forget the look of utter relief and thankfulness as he rose to his feet and drew me tenderly to him.

It was not until long afterwards that I learnt that one of my father's prize cactus plants had been behind him that night, and the minutes when he waited for my answer had been spent in pure agony.

Ah, well, I suppose I should have said the same, anyway. Indeed, the knowledge of such bravery and self-restraint could only enhance my admiration and respect for such a man, whose wife I am proud to be.

I have still a relic of that evening. One day, now many years ago, my dear husband gave me a number of his clothes for my village jumble sale. Amongst them was a pair of black evening trousers, in which on examination I found firmly embedded—a cactus prickle! I was determined that the charity should not suffer, so I bought those trousers in for ninepence, and the part where I found the cactus, cut down and beaded by my own hand in a charming design of rabbits eating grass (one of the blades is the actual prickle) now forms my favourite kettle-holder.

Design for

Lady Blanche Coot's Going Away Dress & Coat

CHAPTER VII

EARLY MARRIED LIFE

While there's a wife, there's hope.
Old Saying.

ON the 15th of June, 1893, I was married to Lord Addle in the beautiful little church of Balder, sanctified by so many memorials to dead Coots. In those days girls were more unused to getting married than they are to-day, and I was decidedly nervous ; but beyond putting on black woollen stockings by mistake for the white silk ones laid out for me, I am thankful to say I did not show it. The bridesmaids wore pretty dresses of tartan serge with chip hats to tone trimmed with thistles, and Addle gave them delightful brooches representing bagpipes in tiny seed pearls.

After the wedding we left for Chicory Hall, which my uncle, Lord Seakale, kindly lent us for the honeymoon, and afterwards we took up residence at Bengers, Hert-fordshire, the English seat of the Addles, my husband having left his regiment to look after the estate, which was a large one. My mother-in-law, who had lived there previously, now moved into the Dower House close by, but we were able to have the great privilege of her unfailing wisdom and constant advice on every detail of our lives, which she gave most generously on all occasions. Addle adored her and regarded her word as law. My feelings for her were equally strong and also hers for me. Almost every day she would walk up to the Hall to see how we were getting on and when she was unable to—for she was never strong— she would write the most exquisite letters. I have a boxful of our correspondence to each other from which I select at random a few in order to show not only her beautiful command of English, but something of the perfect relationship existing between us.

' Dower House, Bengers.   July 3rd, 1893.
' MY DEAREST BLANCHE,

' Although I am so tired with the move that I can scarcely hold the pen, I must write this line of welcome to my dear daughter—Welcome to Bengers. I have left everything as I should wish it left for me— I can say no more than that. The little table by the settee in the morning-room has always had ferns on it ever since *I* came to the Hall and I should be very sad if they were ever put in another place. But, of course, dear Blanche, you must do just as you like. The stuffed pheasant on the piano is, I see, losing a little of its sawdust, which I trust Addy will not fail to see to at once. It has a Special Association, being the pheasant shot by Addy's father on the day of his death. He killed it outright, and (his eyesight was poor, you know) the shock brought on a stroke which proved fatal. So you will understand how that pheasant is particularly dear to me.

'Pray see that the blinds are drawn down in the study at 1.45 precisely on a bright day, as I do not wish the sun to fade the patch of ink spilt by Addy's dear brother, Geordie,[1] when he was ten. So many of these memories make leaving Bengers almost unbearable ; but I have never shirked my duty yet, and it is some consolation to feel I shall still be near you both, ready and willing to guide and counsel you as only a mother can.

'I thought I would come up to luncheon to-morrow and help you settle in—but, of course only if I should be welcome.

'Ever your affectionate,
'MARIA ADDLE.'

'Bengers. 4th June.
'MY DEAREST MOTHER,

'Your dear letter of welcome gave Hector and me real joy ! But you must look after your health and not overtire yourself. After the move I would not dream of allowing you to come and help me to-day, though I feel I am being very unselfish in foregoing such a treat. Will you not dine with us to-morrow at 7.30 instead ? Then everything will be a little more straight and we are looking forward to telling you all about our honeymoon and how we spent our days.

[1] The Hon. George McClutch, died after eating gooseberries, 1881.

53

' I do so feel for you in the wrench it must have been to leave Bengers. If old associations are too poignant you must not come here too often and cause yourself pain by reviving sad memories. Addle and I can always come down to the Dower House to see you, which, you may be sure, we shall do at every available opportunity, though just at the moment he expects to be rather busy taking over the estate.

' With fond love,

' Your affectionate daughter,

' BLANCHE.'

' The Dower House.   July 20th, 1894.

' MY DEAREST BLANCHE,

' I feel sure you would wish to be told that on passing through the kitchen gardens to-day I noticed that there is a very large quantity of strawberries and raspberries—more than you could ever need at Bengers —while the peaches are almost dropping off the walls. So many people have only a small garden—no bigger, for instance, than the Dower House has—and it seems a little selfish to let the fruit be wasted just for want of a little trouble.

' Ever your affectionate

' MOTHER.'

' Bengers.   July 21st.

' MY DEAREST MOTHER,

' Thank you for your kind letter, full as always of thought for others. As a matter of fact we were

54

trying to keep the fruit for next week's house party, but the last thing I want to do is to be selfish.

'Would you kindly return the hamper by bearer?

'Your loving

'BLANCHIE.'

'Dower House.   July 21st.

'Only a hurried note, dearest Blanchie, to say— what a delightful surprise! The strawberries and raspberries will be much appreciated and peaches are my favourite fruit. You shouldn't spoil your old mother-in-law so.

'Your devoted

'M. A.'

'The Dower House.   October 8th, 1894.

'MY DEAREST BLANCHIE,

'I was quite horrified on going up to the nursery yesterday afternoon, while you were out, to find a blazing fire such as one would expect in December. Poor little James looked quite red in the face, and though Nannie said it was on account of his having just crawled all round the room for the first time, I decline to believe her.   Indeed, her manner to me was anything but respectful, almost defiant, and I am going to ask you, darling Blanche, if you will give her notice as soon as possible, as her presence really makes my visits to the nursery quite disagreeable, though, of course, I put my feelings aside and think first that darling James has every right to see his grandmother as often as I can manage, with my heart which is rather bad just now, to climb the stairs.

' Dear Blanchie, I am so anxious that you should appreciate to the full the wonderful trust of motherhood. I did when I was your age and you must let me be your mentor and guide in the upbringing of little James and of (I hope soon) his brothers and sisters. No McClutch has ever had less than five children, and if your family falls short of that it will not be Addy's fault, I know.

' Not that I want you to curb your individuality, dearest child. You must feel perfectly free and I will only tell you when I *dis*approve of anything you do. Otherwise I will say nothing.

' Apropos, I don't at all like that blue velvet bonnet that James wears. A baby of nine months should wear nothing but white. I am ordering him a dozen from Swan & Edgar of my own choice and please send me any coloured ones he has for my Poor Fund. I am very short of baby clothes and they do quite well for the lower classes.

' I will come up and see James to-morrow.

' Ever your loving

' MOTHER.'

' Bengers. Oct. 8th, 1894.
' MY DARLING MOTHER,

' How can I thank you enough for your wonderful letter ? It is so blessed to know that you appreciate as I do the privilege of a mother to bring up her own child. I am deeply grieved that you find Nannie's manner disrespectful, but still more grieved to hear you are feeling your heart, and I have told Jenkins in future to send for James to come down to the drawing-room as soon as you arrive. Of course, this can't be done when he is having his meals or his rest or being put to bed ; so I think it would be best, dearest, if you only came to see him after tea, between five and six.

'How *dear* of you to send me the bonnets. I am so sorry you are short of things for the Poor Fund. I have ordered a box of baby garments to be sent down to you from Swears & Wells for it. I would so gladly send you James's coloured bonnets but they were given me by an aunt.

'*Don't* come to-morrow, darling Mother. James is starting a slight cold, I think, and I wouldn't for the world expose you to infection.

'Your most loving
'BLANCHE.'

'Frosbitten Hall, Norfolk.   March 2nd, 1897.
'MY DARLING BLANCHIE,

'I only heard to-day from Hannah, who has instructions to write and tell me everything that goes on in my absence, that you have the upholsterers in the drawing-room at Bengers. My dearest child, I cannot help feeling a little hurt that you should have taken such a big step without consulting me. Those covers have been there for fifteen years, and even apart from the extravagance in having new ones so soon, it is, surely, obvious that your new choice is of the utmost importance to me. My cough has not nearly gone yet, and this shock has indeed set back my recovery, but I am cutting short my visit here and returning home on Monday. Evie Caister quite understands. She is such a dear and has all the sympathy and finer feelings that I fear the younger generation lacks.

> ' Your ever loving
> ' MOTHER.'

> ' Bengers. Friday.

' BELOVED MOTHER,

    ' I write in haste to *beg* you not to cut short your visit on account of the drawing-room. Your health comes before everything and you looked so ill before you left that Hector and I feel you ought to stay in the Norfolk air as long as possible, though no words can say what it is like here without you.

' Darling, I am so *miserable* that I have hurt you, but indeed it was only that I feared you were not well enough to have the worry of the decision about the covers. Please forgive me and please, *please* do stay on as long as Lady Caister can have you if you want to please

> ' Your most loving and contrite
> ' BLANCHE.'

Alas! my mother-in-law disregarded my entreaties and not only came home before she was nearly well, but, immediately on arrival, tired as she was, insisted on walking up to Bengers in a biting wind to see the covers. She did not care for them unfortunately, and this further upset her—she always took things so terribly to heart—so the next day she became really ill. Bronchitis and heart trouble developed and on the following Wednesday she passed away, leaving us stunned by the suddenness of it all.

Bengers seemed so dreadfully full of her memories and impregnated with her personality, that after a few weeks I felt I could bear it no longer, and so had every single room redecorated, and rearranged every piece of furniture in the house.

A few wrinkles for the home which I have collected and evolved myself during my sixty-seven years and gladly pass on for the benefit of others.

How to bring up fur muffs.   Sprinkle them thoroughly with hot salt and leave them by a bucket of cold water overnight.   The salt will cause the hairs to stretch out eagerly towards the water and the muff will look like new the next morning.

How to avoid a shiny nose if you think it wrong, as many do, to use face powder.   Rub the affected part gently with sand-paper before retiring.

Looking after invalids.   The best ways of helping them.

(1) Reading.   Always reflect that the invalid may not recover and that this may be your last chance of influencing them for good.   Read what will turn their thoughts to serious things, and, without being in any way tactless, before you leave the sick-room just glance at their temperature chart and shake your head.   This will be quite enough to put the idea into their minds.

(2) Talking.   On the other hand, always talk brightly and try to draw their attention from themselves by

telling them some amusing or interesting event you have just experienced yourself, particularly one which they have missed by being in bed, so that they will feel really interested. If you have ever been ill yourself, it is a good thing to tell them about it, if possible somewhat magnifying (without actually being guilty of untruth, of course) the seriousness of your own case, so as to make them feel they have not really been ill at all in comparison. I have had several visitors, taken ill in my house, who, when I have given them rather detailed descriptions of my own maladies, have immediately declared themselves sufficiently recovered to get up and go home the next day.

A charming idea for a fireplace in summer. A screen made of dried and cleaned fishbones, woven together with coloured raffia or wool to tone with your room. At the corners put gilded fir-cones.

Two health drinks.

(1) Cabbage Water. Soak the stalks of a spring cabbage in cold weak tea for some hours. Add a pinch of Epsom salts and a dessert spoonful of syrup of figs. You will find it clears the system of all impurities (except, alas, moral ones !).

(2) Nut Cup. Try this on your very thirsty guests after lawn tennis.

Tell your butler to put all the nutshells he can find after dessert in boiling water overnight, adding in anything else left over from dinner—crusts, plumstones.

etc. It is a wonderfully economical drink, and if iced well does not really taste at all unpleasant.

Hints on table decoration.

Now that this delightful art is coming into fashion again, and I am told that one decorator employs dead flowers and sticks to procure her effects, it may be interesting to describe some of the schemes I have designed myself, having always taken a special pride and pleasure in this most artistic custom.

The Garden. A formal design with little troughs of low growing flowers arranged to look like flower beds. In the centre a small pile of new-mown grass and dead leaves, flanked by miniature watering-cans. Round the edge, at a comfortable distance from the diners, a silver trellis to represent a rustic fence, with fondants stuck through the holes.

The Cave. This is just a simple scheme of rocks and roots arranged in charming profusion all over the table and piled high in the centre. From between the rocks peep forth ferns innumerable. At the end of dinner a string, which has been previously arranged, may be pulled sharply so as to bring the whole centre nest of rocks tumbling down to the amusement and delight of all.

The Sea-shore. A few yards of blue chiffon down the centre of the table in which pretty shells nestle, will give the illusion of sea. You border it with a little strip of sand (slightly damped, otherwise it will blow into the guests' food) and outside the sand, all the sponges that the house can provide. The guests can add to the border their own oyster shells, lobster claws, etc., which contributes much to the marine atmosphere. Use doilies painted with fishes and drape a little dried seaweed over the menus.

CHAPTER VIII

INDIA

Lo ! the poor Indian.
A. Pope : ' Essay on Man.'

AFTER the birth of my second son, Hector, in 1898, I did not seem able to pick up my usual health and spirits again, and the doctors urged a long sea voyage. It so happened that this coincided with an invitation from some old friends of my husband's, Riggles and Cuckoo Twilfit,[1] to go out and pay them a visit in Poona, as he had just been appointed Governor of the Bombay Presidency. Addle was at first uncertain whether he could manage to accompany me, for he took his duties as a landowner very seriously and was always down at the estate office punctually at twelve noon every third Friday. Eventually, however, he said, with his usual loving consideration, that my health was almost as important as the estate ; so having handed over the children to the care of my sister, Soppy, who had only eight of her own[2] and so was

---

[1] Sir Richard and Lady Twilfit.

[2] Her family has now remained at eleven for some time, and it is feared there will be no more. It is a great grief to them both.

delighted for them to have some companionship, we packed up and set sail on September 16th in the s.s. *Boadicea*.

The voyage was made especially delightful by the presence on board of Mr. Bertram and Lady Vica (Victoria) Ogle. B.O., as he was always called, was the well-known wit and the funniest person, with the exception of my brother Humpo, that I have ever come across. As may be imagined his brilliant sallies were the *piéces de résistance* of the trip, and were passed on from passenger to passenger even as far as the second class. How we laughed ! When we passed the Rock of Gibraltar, he said, ' What a rocky feller '— Rockefeller being a name very much in the public mouth just then. A young honeymoon couple on board he alluded to as ' the turtle doves', because they were so devoted, and to a friend who was recounting to him how she went shopping one day and had a hansom back, he remarked : ' Personally, I'd sooner have a handsome face.' Real, rapier-like wit of that calibre is now a thing of the past, I fear.

We arrived at Bombay on October 5th and were met by my cousin, Ribby Coot[1] who was stationed there. He showed us all the sights of the town, including the famous sacred cockroaches, which are kept in an exquisite miniature palace of carved coral—a perfect background for their shining black skins—and fed at sunrise and sundown on gnats' eggs. We were told

[1] Captain Ribston Coot, 5th Gurkhas.

that they are rapidly becoming extinct, mainly owing to the fact that cockroaches cannot live on gnats' eggs, which is very sad.

The following morning we entrained for Poona. Immediately we entered the carriage we saw that it had another occupant—a lady. She was a very striking-looking woman, so small that her feet scarcely touched the carriage floor, unless, of course, she stood up. But her eyes glowed like coals of fire in the fine oblong of her face, and her sensitive hands kept pulling up the window and letting it down as though she were in the grip of some tremendous emotion.

We soon got into conversation and I was struck by her intimate knowledge of Indian life and her vivid way of talking. She had a habit of emphasizing her points by bringing down her fist on one's knee to punctuate every sentence, which was very telling. Her life's mission was evidently the emancipation of women and she had been brave enough to ruin her marriage for the cause. For on her honeymoon, she told us, she felt it her duty to give lectures on the subject to the female hotel servants. She gave them in her bedroom every evening after dinner for five nights, and on the sixth her husband left her, never to return. Since then circumstances had led her to India, where, with great enthusiasm, she had taken up the cause of the Indian women in purdah. She was just then on a tour to the various Presidencies to try and enlist the sympathy of the Governors in a scheme for teaching knitting to the Zenanas.

As she talked, I felt something innate and elemental rise up within me and demand outlet. It was a hic-cough which, as I have mentioned before, is always a sign of emotion in our family. Eagerly I said that we were on our way to stay at Government House, Poona, and would do all in our power to help her in her wonderful work. I was about to ask her if she had enough financial backing for her enterprise, when Addle had a sudden and quite unaccountable fit of coughing and by the time he had recovered we were almost at Poona. But we parted with great friendliness and promises of meeting again. Little did I think then how my whole outlook and even the course of my life were to be changed by that chance encounter. Such is fate and such was the entry into my life of the cele-brated Agatha Slubb-Repp.[1]

The Twilfits gave us a warm welcome and we were soon immersed in the enchantment of Indian life, every moment of which I enjoyed from *chota hazri* to the nightly *burra khana*, or watching the sundown from the Bombay Yacht Club, or listening up-country to the wail of the *hamal* floating out across the compound. Worthier pens than mine have described the glories of the enchanted East, so I will not attempt it, beyond saying that the things that impressed me most—I may be unusual in this—were the intense heat (except during

[1] No connexion with the Slub-Reps.

A CHARMING STUDY OF AGATHA SLUBB-REPP

the cool weather), the amazing cold of some of the nights (though they could, of course, be very warm), the astonishing shortness of the Eastern twilight, and the Taj Mahal by moonlight. The far-famed rope trick I never actually managed to see myself; but our host's secretary had a great friend in Pachmari whose son-in-law declared that he saw it with his own eyes, less than six feet away, in Hyderabad; so I think there can be no doubt about it that it is quite genuine.

My husband had some splendid shikars, which he enjoyed enormously. He just missed a tiger, but got a perfect shot at the tethered kid and brought it down in one. His skin—the kid's, I mean—now looks very fine as a rug in our telephone-room.

But by far the greatest event of our Indian visit was, to me, my friendship with Mrs. Slubb-Repp and the work I was able to do for the S.P.P.H.[1] We soon encountered this amazing woman again, as indeed she seemed to be everywhere. Social barriers did not trouble her one bit, and when she did not know people she engineered an introduction on the slenderest pretext, in order to further her work by talking about it incessantly. I thought it splendid of her, but several stiff-necked Britishers were very unsympathetic about it, including, I am sorry to say, my husband, who never really liked her or approved of my association with her at all. But this did not damp my enthusiasm in the

[1] Society for the Promotion of Purdah Hobbies.

least, and I am proud to think I was able to do some good work with some of the younger women, teaching them to crochet. I was not quite up to the more advanced tuition of knitting, so left that to my leader.

It was, of course, very difficult to obtain permission to enter the Zenanas, and we sometimes had recourse to innocent deceptions, which on one occasion landed me in an adventure that was most unpleasant, to say the least of it, and might have had very serious consequences indeed.

We had been invited one afternoon by the vastly rich Nizam of Chortlepugger to visit his summer palace, in order to hear his famous singing elephants—the breeding of which is permitted to his family alone. It was, of course, supposed to be a purely social visit, but, knowing the Nizam had over four hundred wives in his Zenana, I was determined to be prepared for action, and so slipped a ball of wool and some crochet pins underneath my *solar topee* in case of need.

It was a wonderful sight to see the splendid great beasts, heavily caparisoned in purple and gold, lifting up their trunks and quite distinctly singing ' God Save the Queen '. In honour of us they also sang ' Annie Laurie ' and ' Drink to me only '. It was during the latter that, seeing the attention of all so thoroughly occupied, I contrived to slip away and make my way to the Zenana, the position of which I knew well from maps I had been shown by Agatha Slubb-Repp.

How I avoided being stopped by guards I shall never know—I suppose Heaven helps those who dare for their cause. But the fact remains that I managed to penetrate three out of the many courts of the palace and to teach the rudiments of crochet to no less than eighteen dear girls. Their touching amusement and interest in the proceeding was sufficient proof, if I needed one, of the greatness of my leader's mission. But I suppose it was wellnigh impossible to expect to get out as easily as I got in. What happened I cannot quite say ; there was a sudden commotion, and before I could resist I was hurried away, down a long marble corridor, and into a large room, where several serving women were in attendance. There, despite my violent protests, I was undressed and given the sweet sulphur bath which, from books I had read on the subject, I immediately recognized to my horror as one of the earlier preparations for new wives.

It was a terrible situation. I was rubbed all over with sacred frog-oil, my eyelids and ears were dyed, my hair dipped in scented camel's milk, and all sorts of other most embarrassing things of which I would prefer not to write. The dreadful part of it was that my cries for help only met with tolerant grins from the women, as though they were a common occurrence. It was not until the main preparations were over and I was lying on a couch having my finger and toe-nails painted a vulgar red, that my continued distress seemed to strike them as unusual. The chief eunuch was summoned and I was at once released. He explained, with abject apologies, that a large batch of new wives had arrived the day before and were ordered to be ready by six o'clock that evening. It was thought when they saw me, that one had been mislaid, and that was the reason of the hurried preparations, as it was then five-thirty. Sometimes I still wake up in bed, cold with horror, to think of the narrow escape I had that day.

After that adventure I did no more work for the Zenanas. This was partly due to the fact that my nerves were greatly upset by the episode, and partly by the news of the outbreak of war in South Africa, which occupied all our thoughts and cut short our visit, Addle having to hurry home to rejoin his regiment.

But India will always hold golden memories for me, and I still correspond with several enlightened women, who have been brave enough to emerge from the prison of their purdah and to lead a normal life. Indeed, I have at the moment a wonderful play written by one of them, which I am trying hard to get produced on the English stage. It is striking and beautiful in its originality, having only three characters. Two of them are invisible, having just committed suttee on the altar, whence their voices arise. The third, the old priest who tends the flame, is sworn to eternal silence, so he has a non-speaking part. So far, managers have been singularly dense in their lack of appreciation, but Mr. Cochran has written me a most courteous letter, saying that when he returns from America he hopes to have the privilege of considering it, though he will not be back for some time.

Two of the splendid scenes in the play I have just mentioned. There are fifty-eight of them, each with the same setting and the same players, Hika and Plundra Nil.

SCENE XIX

Hika. I am as the blown seed when it is scattered into forgetfulness. I am nothing.

Plundra. I am less than nothing. I am as the water that has dried upon the eyelid of a cockatoo.

Hika : I am an ocean of nothingness, less than the oblivion of dead spiders, more than the nothingness of an escaped wish-bud.

Plundra. I am nothing.

Hika. Beloved, how was it when the fire touched you ?

Plundra. White and white and white.

Hika. Look up, little apple of my tired loins. What do you see ?

Plundra. I see the heart of a cocoon that is spun about all my yesterdays. I see the tendril of youth plucking out the eyes of the *chimbak.*[1]

Hika. Do you see the perfumes of our worthiness

[1] *Chimbak,* i.e. Undertaker.

twisting, twisting aloud into the yam-yam blossoms ?

Plundra. Yes, yes. I see them. How blessed is their message. Beloved, do you see them too ?

Hika. I ? I see nothing.

Plundra. Nothing ?

Hika. Less than nothing.

A white frog falls upon the altar—dead.

[CURTAIN]

SCENE XXXVI

The 3,000th Day.

Hika. It is splendid to be dead.

Plundra. We have drunk blood. Whence comes it that the red powder of its flames be not upon the soles of our understanding ?

Hika. Because we are dead.

Plundra. Dead, Dead.

Hika. Death, like a careless water-carrier, has spilt us upon the desert of desire.

Plundra. Death, like twin gardeners, has delved into our lustless remorse.

Hika. The dentist, Death, has plunged his hand into our mouth and gathered the teeth of our coherence.

Plundra. Death, like a scavenger's mate——

Hika. I am weary of similes.

Plundra.   I too.   Let us use no more.

Hika.   Let us instead wind our love-songs about the lamp-posts of passion.

Plundra.   Let us be as the mystic rabbits, eating up time.

A sigh is heard, as of a dying drummer boy's wings.

[CURTAIN]

CHAPTER IX

MIPSIE

A good woman is a wondrous creature, cleaving to the right
and to the good under all change.

Life of Tennyson.

IT seems hopelessly inadequate to devote only two
short chapters to Mipsie when several volumes could
be written about her enchanting loveliness, her talents,
and her strange vivid life. It was, above all, Life
which she loved—loved so passionately that it led her
into paths which would, possibly, have been better left
untrodden. But ' *tout comprendre est tout pardoner*',
and I hope in this short space to throw a new and
more intimate light on some of the events in her life
which made the world talk so much, and sometimes
so unkindly.

It was in spring of 1902 that I first began to realize
that things were not going right between her and Oxo,
chiefly through his fault, I must say. While he was
fighting in South Africa, Mipsie had done the obviously
sensible thing which was to save the vast expense of
Brisket Castle by shutting it up and taking a house
in Paris instead. He raised no objection at the time,
yet on his return, although Mipsie came home within

six months, which was as soon as she could manage to wind up her affairs in France, he was furious and practically refused to pay her Paris debts. He actually seemed to expect her to have existed there on the same money as she would have lived on at Brisket, which was frankly ridiculous. That was the beginning of the rift. The next quarrel was over the children. There were two, a girl and a boy, whom Mipsie worshipped and made a point of seeing at least twice a week. But she was always adorably vague and one day when Soppy and her family of eight were staying there Mipsie lifted up little Archie Hogshead and said to a caller : ' This is my baby.' It was a very natural mistake to make—they were, after all, first cousins—but Oxo chose to take umbrage and accused her of not knowing which were her own children. Mipsie, with her flashing wit, tried to ease matters by a playful rejoinder : ' Well, how do you know which are yours ? ' but he was too angry to be soothed. The breach widened.

The end came over a stupid misunderstanding. Mipsie was expected back from Brussels, where she had been on a visit, to act as hostess to a large shooting party at Brisket, but was taken suddenly ill and telegraphed : ' Cannot return. In bed with *migraine*.' Oxo, who was always a very poor French scholar, had never heard of the word, so completely misconstruing the contents of the message rushed frantically to Brussels, where, as bad luck would have it, Mipsie's

MIPSIE AT HER LOVELIEST

attack had suddenly subsided and she was trying to revive her strength for the journey by a quiet little dinner with an old friend in the private room of an hotel. Explanations were all in vain. After a distressing scene of violent recriminations on both sides Oxo left for England, and we learnt that they had separated.

Poor darling brave Mipsie! What she must have suffered during the divorce proceedings, losing not only her good name but her children and the famous Brisket pearls as well as having her allowance cut down to a beggarly £3,000 a year, I dread to think. She was always so sensitive and so proud—the pride of a thoroughbred—and hated to fall short of any standard or ideal she had set for herself. That was the reason why she accepted the offer of Fr. 50,000 a year as an allowance from another old friend, the Marquis de Pelouse. It was to enable her to live as Oxo, in the days when he had loved her, would have liked her to. It was amazing loyalty for a woman who had been treated as Mipsie had ; yet the world said malicious and bitter things even about that.

She soon married again. She never could bear loneliness and plenty of men were only too willing. Her second husband was Sir Constant Standing, a baronet of good family and a nice fellow, but somewhat weak and easily persuaded and far from clever. He had a comfortable income but quite inadequate to keep up the beautiful villa which they—especially Mipsie— had set their hearts on at Monte Carlo. It would really have been wiser if he had said so straight away instead of struggling on and attempting to recover by gambling, for which he had no aptitude whatever, or even liking. In fact he had never played at all until Mipsie taught him to, as she taught him many other things.

However, they were happy enough for a time and people seeing them together have often said what a wonderful wife she was and how she would never put on even the smallest stake at the tables without asking him for the money first. She tried to do him good in many other ways too, encouraging him to take life more seriously and put his back into some regular occupation and as a result he worked so hard on a system at baccarat that he spent a great deal more money than he should in testing it, and the worry of it produced a bad nervous breakdown, which made life even harder for my poor sister.

But it was not until after his bankruptcy that Mipsie began to realize that Constant was not, somehow, the same man as she thought she had married. I think it all came as rather a shock to her. And then she found out that the vastly rich uncle who had been intending to leave all his money to him had changed his will when Constant had declared his intention of marrying Mipsie and that quite broke her up. The cruelty of the uncle in taking that line just because she had the misfortune to be badly treated by her first husband, and above all the deceit, the base dishonesty of Constant in marrying her without telling her of the changed will—he gave the paltry excuse that he ' Didn't want to worry her and thought the old boy would come round '—were too much for my sister, who was always the soul of honour. She felt she could no longer live with one who had wounded and disappointed her so greatly and in the summer of 1906 she left him. I am told he has gone sadly downhill since that date. He now lives at Cannes and is to be found every day in a not very reputable bar where he will say to the merest stranger : ' Have I ever told you about my wife ? ' He will then proceed to use such indecent language that even the visitors from Palm Beach cannot stand it.

But to return to my sister. After she had procured her divorce she passed through a time of great loneliness and hardship, struggling to live on the pittance allowed her by Brisket, augmented only by gifts from one or two friends, and without any real background to her life. There were happy times, of course, for she was always incurably gay, but sometimes she longed for security again—some one of solid worth to fall back upon in every necessity. It was, I think, this instinctive craving for safety that prompted her to decide to go to America. She was greatly attracted by what she heard of the satisfactory and solid nature of American home life at that date, and her always vivid imagination was caught by an exquisite diamond-studded vanity-box which she had been shown by a friend and told it was a favour given in a cotillion at Newport, which was

picturesquely known as ' the Millionaires' playground '.
The idea of such fairy godmother presents being given
at a mere ball appealed to the childish, almost elfin
element in her nature and she, of course, always adored
beauty in any form.   I remember how once during a
house party at Coots Balder, when we were girls and
shared a room, I woke three nights running to discover
Mipsie's bed empty, and each time when she returned
she told me she had been in the garden listening to the
nightingales.   I longed to share her joy and begged to
go with her one night, but she said the nightingales
sang a different song for her, which I thought a
charming whimsy.   She was, indeed, a child of nature.

Had she gone to America that autumn her life might
have been very different, for with her birth and beauty
and brilliance she would soon, I am convinced, have
been queen of the Four Hundred and perhaps married
happily, though, of course, an American husband would
have been rather a shock to the family !   But once
again it was her very womanhood—those qualities of
sweet unselfishness and generosity that made her what
she was—which directed her destiny otherwise.

She was actually on the eve of departure.   I had lent
her the money for her ticket as some of her investments
had been giving her trouble—when at a soirée given
by the Russian Ambassador in London a very old man
was introduced to her as Prince Fédor Ubetzkoi, and
with her invariable charming courtesy to the aged, who
as she rightly says are often worth so much more than

the younger generation—she sat and conversed with him in an alcove for a while. As they talked she became more and more impressed by his courtly manner and distinguished bearing and found her eyes riveted by the beauty of his finely-modelled hands, their delicate tapering fingers set off to perfection by the simple severity of two uncut emeralds the size of pigeons' eggs. Gently she drew him out about himself in the winning way she knew so much better than any one, and when she learnt that he owned the whole of Goulashia with its vast platinum mines, that he was seventy-nine and a widower with one of the most beautiful palaces in Europe full of world-famous treasures, her whole woman's heart went out to the poor old man ; his loneliness amidst such great possessions, his helplessness, his very age appealed to something deep within her. She could not bear to think of him growing nearer the grave each day, perhaps without even the consolation of knowing that after his death his treasures would give joy to some one dear to him. With characteristic impulsiveness she threw all her previous plans to the winds. She saw her duty, her destiny, clearly before her. Within a week they were married and the Prince and Princess Fédor Ubetzkoi had left for the palace at Ekaterinbog.

PRINCE FÉDOR'S TREASURES

Mipsie told me that the treasures of Ekaterinbog Palace came up to her fullest expectations. The walls were lined with Old Masters, some of which she was able to recognize from their famous originals in the Louvre and elsewhere. Experts came from all over the world to see the equestrian portrait of Charles I by Van Eyck, and the famous collection, formed by Prince Fédor's father, of oleographs from Landseer. The ballroom, designed as a grotto, was made entirely of Dresden china ; while each step of the grand stair-case was of a different coloured marble, quarried from the Ubetzkoi domains—a lovely rainbow effect, making a gay contrast to the carved platinum banisters and handrail.

Every room contained *objets d'art* which would have dignified any museum. Perhaps the most interesting to a foreigner was the array of assassination daggers, as the right to wear them had been conferred on the family by the Czarina Elizabeth for their share in the removal of one of her lovers. The Ubetzkois, always a powerful landowning family, had indeed played their part in Russian history, and the palace was full of reminiscences of it. One local custom was recalled by a case of beautiful knouts, the exquisite chasing of their silver handles worn smooth with use. By the great stove in each room stood a rack, also of solid silver, on which a knout was always suspended, so that the prince should never have to go from one room to another if he wanted to flog a serf.

In many ways the finest thing in the house was also an imperial gift. Prince Fédor's grandfather had been a grand chamberlain in the times of the Nihilists, and lost his life in a bomb outrage, when his resplendent carriage was mistaken for that of the Czar. In sympathetic recognition of his services the Czar presented the family with a large model of the bomb in gold, which stood on a malachite base in the entrance hall. It was over seven feet high, and very picturesque, Mipsie said.

THE FOLKSONG WHICH WAS COMPOSED
IN MIPSIE'S HONOUR

Yumpa ! yumpa ! oglo pzrhwlt !
Brisketinski Fédor bgmkwlt.
Lappup vodka, būzov grog.
Yumpa hak Ekaterinbog !

CHAPTER X

MIPSIE AGAIN

Hope deferred maketh the heart sick.
Proverbs xii. 12.

I ALWAYS think one of the greatest tragedies of life is a really noble action that goes unrewarded and even misunderstood. It is, of course, impossible to blame Prince Fédor for part of that very senility that had so appealed to Mipsie's sympathy, but it was unfortunate, to say the least of it, that his memory was so bad and that he entirely forgot to mention that he had two children by his previous marriage, a daughter of forty-one, Irina, who ruled almost as Queen at the Palace of Ekaterinbog, and a son of twenty-five, Michel, who would inherit Goulashia and everything in it, on his father's death. So that for a time it seemed almost as if my sister's sacrifice were in vain and she felt it very deeply, I think. But out of sorrow and disappointment sometimes joy emerges and this was now the case for Mipsie, who certainly needed a little happiness after all she had gone through. With wonderful philosophy she accepted the situation as she found it and calmly and dispassionately set to work to think out where her duty lay. At once she saw that the future of Goulashia was the vital thing. Fédor was old, and still, in spite of marriage, under his daughter's thumb. But Michel was young and impressionable and the future heir. Mipsie knew instinctively that she could best influence her adopted country through him and she now concentrated, with all the charm and ability of her command, on winning his allegiance and affection.

She was abundantly successful; for two years—from 1909–1911—there followed for my sister what she still refers to, with tears in her eyes, as the happiest time in her life, and one of the most perfect relationships I have ever encountered. She has allowed me to reprint excerpts from her diary of the time which show something of the beauty of that friendship.

'Ekaterinbog. Sept. 12th, 1909.

'Woke early, before 11, with my heart singing "Mich is coming to-day". He drove out to lunch, bringing me an immense bouquet of roses, and we went for a long ride afterwards, seen off by Irina, with a face like a thunder-cloud, but who cares! Mich was as sweet as ever. He says I am his good angel and when he reigns over Goulashia he will never do anything without my approval. I am so happy to feel I can help.

'Nov. 3rd. The Palace Ball to-night. Mich sent me a lovely ruby star which was perfect on my new Paquin. How happy I am. Irina looked revolting in purple poplin.'

It is a pity that Princess Irina never managed to win her affection. I am certain it cannot have been Mipsie's fault. The next entry I had selected at random shows something of the difficulties of her life, of which her friendship with Michel (often spoken of very harshly by unkind people) was the only happy side.

' July 18th, 1910. How tired I am of it all. This dull old Palace, Fédor's everlasting recollections of the past, Irina's sulks, the sameness of it. Thank Heaven, Mich is coming for the week-end. I really am over-done and need a holiday badly.

' July 19th. Spoke to Fédor about a holiday and he was quite reasonable though he tried for a bit to suggest coming too, but I told him travelling is much too tiring for him. I suggested a month at Baden-Baden. He agrees. What a prospect !

' July 21st. Mich came to-day. He looks tired and overdone though as sweet as ever. I told him he should have a change of air.

' July 22nd. Such a lovely day. Rode with Mich and broke it to him that I was going away. He was too touching and said he couldn't bear it and why shouldn't he come too ? I think it *might* be rather a good plan as he really does not look well. I said we would speak to his father about it after Irina had retired.

' July 23rd. It is all fixed and Mich and I with a

small staff go to Baden-Baden next week. Hooray! Fédor quite agreed about the importance of Mich's health—at least I think he did, but he was so sleepy. Anyway, he consented, and couldn't be bothered to alter his decision even when Irina tried to make him, on hearing the news this morning. I wonder why she detests me so.

' Baden-Baden. Aug. 12th. Spent a perfect day with Mich at my side every minute and more devoted than ever. I tell him he shouldn't waste his time with an old woman of thirty-four,[1] but he only laughs and says no girl of eighteen can hold a candle to me. Foolish boy.

' Aug. 19th. Mich gave me the most exquisite diamond-and-sapphire bracelet to-day. How very beautiful life is.

' Aug. 28th. Nothing could be more perfect than this life. Mich is talking of making a settlement on me. It makes me proud to think how he trusts and looks up to me. Only three days more. I must make the most of them.'

Alas, that was the nearest Prince Michel ever got to making the settlement on Mipsie which she so richly deserved. They were recalled next day because Prince Fédor developed a chill, which proved to be very slight. But soon after that other troubles began to appear.

[1] Mipsie must have made a mistake here. She was thirty-seven in 1910.

The very strength of Mipsie's devotion to her step-son brought about worries which acted as a canker to her happiness, eventually destroying it.   In November 1910, she writes :

' Had a most worrying day.   Telephoned to Mich as usual and remarked on his seeming *distrait*.   He denied it, but after a bit confessed that he had just been over to lunch with the Nastikoffs, who have never been at all friendly to me, so it was rather disloyal of him.   He further said that Xenia, the ugly little round daughter, had grown into a lovely and charming girl.   Don't believe a word of it and told him I didn't trust Prince Nastikoff or any of them a yard.   Mich seemed very upset.

' Nov. 25th.   A cold raw day.   How I loathe Ekaterinbog in winter.   Mich came over to lunch, but couldn't or wouldn't ride as he said he must get back quickly.   I was very disappointed and burst into tears. He was sweet but left early all the same.

' Dec. 12th.   Is life worth while ?   I wrote a long letter to Mich saying that I hadn't seen him for a fort-night and had I lost a friend.   Worry for the future, and fear that he will make an unfortunate marriage are making me ill.   Why must all lovely things end ?

' Dec. 15th.   Mich writes and just says : " Don't be silly."   Silly, *me* !   I am furious.

' Dec. 19th.   The blow has fallen.   Mich is going to

marry Xenia Nastikoff. I have told him he will be miserable and I know she is not the wife for him, but he won't listen to me. To make it worse, Fédor and Irina seem delighted. I am utterly wretched.'

In March the following year she wrote : ' Mich married. Our wonderful friendship is over and my happiness gone.' It almost breaks my heart to read of such suffering. It was amazing devotion for a step-mother to have given.

Mich's marriage seemed to have the effect of making her turn again very much to her husband who was becoming increasingly frail and for two long weary years she scarcely left his side. He died in 1914, leaving her quite comfortably off, though the bulk of his vast fortune went, of course, to Michel. She left Goulashia, which was hateful to her with past memories, and went to live in Paris until the war, when she plunged herself in war work like all of us. One day news came to her of the Russian Revolution. The palace at Ekaterinbog had been seized. Mich and his family had fled. ' Then what will happen about my money ? ' asked poor Mipsie desperately. She was told it was not worth the paper it was printed on. She was ruined, except for £3,000 a year.

After the war she revived her old plan of going to the U.S.A. Although it was not the same as the America of the golden days, she felt she craved ' fresh woods and pastures new ' after all she had suffered in

Europe. Besides, her allowance from Brisket was worth even less now and she was hard put to it to keep body and soul together. So with superb pluck she set to work to earn her living by giving her name to trade advertisements, and the face that had launched a thousand cheques was now seen in every paper, recommending soap and patent foods and toilet preparations. What it must have cost her—a Coot, a Duchess and a Princess—I hate to think, but *noblesse oblige* was part of her very being.

However, romance was not quite over for my dear sister. Even in that land of hard cash love can bloom. She met one day, on business, Mr. Julius K. Block of Block's Skin Bleaching Cream. He had been very struck by Mipsie's photograph in a dentifrice campaign and came to ask her to pose for his cream. Something about his childlike simplicity combined with his undoubted stability and business integrity struck a chord in her weary heart. She saw him again—and again. And then one day he took her to his magnificent home in Fifth Avenue and she sat on a Gobelin settee while he told her of his country home in Long Island. As he spoke of the solid lapis swimming pool his face lit up with boyish enthusiasm. In that instant she knew that she loved again.

For a few years they were very happy. Then again cruel fate intervened. The rage for sun-bathing and outdoor sports came in and with it the decline in the fashion for white skin. Block's bleaching cream went

93

smash and Mipsie's husband was a ruined man. He felt he couldn't face going back and telling her the news. They found him in his office, shot through the head . . . once again Mipsie was a widow and practically penniless.

It is small wonder that after this last tragedy my poor sister felt despair knocking at her heart. But her life had taught her nothing if not resignation. In 1930 she decided to give up the world, which had let her down so badly, and become a decorator. With the remnants of the Block money she opened the establishment in Mayfair which she still carries on, under the name of *MIPSIE BRISKET*. She felt that as she had had no previous experience of decorating and her mind was not confused with any historical or artistic knowledge she would come fresh to it and the public would benefit by entirely new ideas. The first room she decorated proved the truth of her theory—it was like nothing else on earth, as one critic said—and her *clientèle* grew rapidly each season, so that, with the occasional help of old friends, she now manages to live quite comfortably, I am thankful to say, and has had particular success with her unseasoned wood furniture. She is still the same gay, delightful, sympathetic Mipsie, though, to one who has known her all her life, it is clear that her troubles have set their mark upon her, her hair, on one occasion, having turned chestnut in a single night.

I reprint a newspaper cutting by ' Melisande ' of that attractive paper, *Venus at Home*, which describes some of Mipsie's work and the success which she so well deserves.

' Of recent cocktail parties one of the most successful and amusing happened yesterday when Sir " Oggie " Trevor gave a house-warming in his lovely new Curzon Street flat, so delightfully decorated by Mipsie Brisket, who was there in person, of course, looking as arresting as usual in a simple little black-and-scarlet creation of Punchinello's with an alluring spiral design on it. Over this went a superb mink coat which the Duchess told us was a gift—and one that was richly deserved, I'm sure.   Other well-knowns at the party were Lord Robert (Bonzo) Bingham and his new American wife— all silver foxes and quite lovely, I thought ; Una, Lady Lowestoft, with the latest " moth-eaten " coiffure which suits her so perfectly ; and the Michel Ubetzkois, who were telling every one about their new darling little butcher's shop in Shepherd Market, which looks like getting all the Mayfair custom.   Then young Archie Hogshead was there—just back from Hollywood and pleasantly tanned by the arc lights ; and the Randall

Twins, Michael and David, whom, when they wear the same make-up, you really *cannot* tell apart ; and swarms more of the smart eligibles and young marrieds and amusing intelligents, so that the party rapidly spread far beyond the one vast sitting-room on to the roof, which clever Mipsie has disguised as a Venetian scene with striped awnings, and gondolas to sit in.

' The chief note of the flat is originality too. So into a colour scheme of royal blue and Rose du Barry—it is well known that she only uses colours which have some royal connexion—she has boldly introduced silvered bamboo furniture with little bows of scarlet ribbon at the notches which give a very gay and festive effect. She herself designed the large piece of furniture which occupies the whole of one wall, and contains not only the usual cocktail bar and radio-gram which are concealed in every modern piece, but a make-up cabinet—so useful for lady guests—a roulette board, and even a bed, in case of immediate need.

' The bedroom is in quieter tones, being confined to Romanoff Malachite and Medici red with a striking note of colour in the pictures, which are mosaics of coloured looking-glass, designed by the Duchess, representing Leda with various swans and Europa surrounded by bulls.

' But the bathroom was the greatest triumph. The walls are painted with scenes from the *Thousand and One Nights*, hot and cold water flows from the hands of two aluminium odalisques, and if you press a little carved black boy the bell rings—all very ingenious and attractive.

'There was lovely food and lovely drink as usual at "Oggie's" parties and none of us tore ourselves away till later than we should—and then we left the Duchess still saying good-bye to her host.'

CHAPTER XI

THE WOMEN'S SUFFRAGE MOVEMENT

England hath need of thee.
Wordsworth.

I MUST now return to a phase of my life, on which I look back to-day with mingled pride and regret, for there was both pleasure and pain, glory and disillusionment attached to it—I mean, the part I played in English history in the summer of 1908 as a militant for the cause of Women's Enfranchisement.

I had always been a great admirer of our sex. From my earliest childhood's days I used to note how my dear mother, without losing any of her womanly charm, would make even the butler quake by a few well-chosen words and could control my father by a mere look. If this failed, she could get anything she wanted by bursting into tears, a talent she cultivated and developed to such perfection, that it used to strike me—child as I was—that such capabilities deserved a larger sphere of influence than the home alone. This impression of woman's superiority was further confirmed after my marriage by observation of my mother-in-law and her perfect ascendancy over Addle. I revised in my mind all that I had read and been taught about men being

99

the strong sex. Are these the creatures, I remember thinking, who are supposed to be the rulers of the world ? Why, they don't know the A B C of managing other people's affairs, compared with women ! And then and there, I suppose, was born that desire to champion the women's cause, which, encouraged by my work in India and fanned into a flame of indignation against men in general by Mipsie's unhappy experiences, found vent in the great fight of 1906–1914 for Women's Rights—the Right to a legitimate outlet for her natural instinct to interfere, the Right to talk, that God-implanted urge that is so strong in each one of our sex.

Even so, I might never have taken an active part in the militant movement, had it not been for Addle's long absence in Norway on a fishing expedition. I had, of course, been doing my bit in the county, organizing village meetings and sewing bees, at which I read the workers' delightful extracts from *Drawing Blood*, by ' One Who's Done It,' and as a result of which we were able to send up to head-quarters 200 flags, 75 spectacle-cases, 150 hatpins and 35 tobacco pouches of our colours (the last being all returned on our hands and subsequently made into flower mats). I had often tried to get Addle to take the chair at meetings, but he developed at that time a bad attack of sciatica, which often became quite acute towards the evening, so that he was prevented from accompanying me every time. Finally, he said that he thought nothing but a change would really cure him, and as a result fixed up this Norwegian tour with an old friend and brother-officer. It was very sad for me, as it was just after I had told him of my plans for a summer campaign, to include a whole suffrage week, in which I was counting on him to act as a sandwichman. Being the squire, he would have been a tremendous draw, and now the whole thing had to be upset. But, of course, I put his health first, as we wives always do. And in many ways, I reflected, I should have a freer hand.

However, the summer campaign at Bengers was destined to be put aside in favour of greater things. For once more, fate intervened. I had come up to London to see my husband off, and afterwards was crossing the station to post some letters, when suddenly, with a thrill, I heard the pillar-box in front of me say in clear tones : ' Votes for Women.' I stood rooted to the spot, while an old lady who had been in the act of posting a letter, screamed loudly. In one moment a crowd had collected and was listening to one of the most impressive things I have ever heard—a magnificent speech from the pillar-box, which was seen to be trembling from mouth to base with emotion. At length a porter rushed up and, as was the way of men at that time, put a sudden end to a perfectly peaceful and legal proceeding by lifting the pillar-box, which was then seen to be a dummy, high in the air, as he did so disclosing the pale, triumphant face—its sallow spirituality vividly thrown up by a splash of scarlet across one cheek—of Agatha Slubb-Repp !

It was lucky I was there, for the police had been summoned, and in another moment might have made an arrest, which indeed was just what Mrs. Slubb-Repp was counting on. But I was adamant. 'No,' I whispered, '*you* are wanted for other work'; and I bore her quickly to my waiting car and home to her cosy little flat in Pimlico, with its broad arrows on the chintzes and its walls hung with pencil studies of forcible feeding. There we were soon joined by Miss Emily Coop, who shared the flat with Agatha, and we sat there for long hours talking of the work and of our aspirations. Suddenly Mrs. Slubb-Repp said : 'Lady Addle, why don't you come up to London and help us in the campaign, while your husband is away ? There is plenty of room for a camp bed in the dining-room, and you could dress in the bathroom—and the cause needs you. *Do* come.'

Work ! Real hard work in London and marches with banners through jostling crowds, and perhaps, who knows, a genuine arrest ? It was a thrilling thought. And then Mrs. Slubb-Repp let out that they were very short of funds, and actually owed a quarter's rent for the flat. That decided me. It was my duty to help—a duty I was proud to fulfil.

It was an intensely interesting time. From the moment we greeted each other every morning with 'Votes for Women', to our good-night salutation of 'Down with Asquith', we were busy for the cause, distributing pamphlets, chalking on pavements, vying

EMILY COOP DOING SPLENDID WORK

with each other in devising schemes for defying authority in some form. Indeed, sometimes the rivalry was even a little bitter—as, for instance, when Agatha, as I now called her, went to the Zoo and thrust a 'Votes for Women' paper into the orang-outang's hand, and on the same day Emily Coop and I made our way into an operating theatre and did the same to a surgeon, just as he was about to remove a Cabinet Minister's appendix. Agatha got a personal commendation from Mrs. Pankhurst next procession day, and we got nothing. Yet ours was infinitely the more dangerous task of the two, because Agatha had bars between her and the animal and we had none.

But on the whole we lived and worked together very happily, our great mission binding us in simple unity, all our energies and intellects turned to one point—how to further the cause by some big coup that would startle the world and even astonish our great leader. But what? What would really rouse the English public and, above all, the English male? My thoughts flew to my husband, who had just written pages in praise of some fish he had caught—and then the idea came to me.

Sport! The one passionate element in an Englishman's otherwise stolid character. That was the thing to attack—better far than biting policemen, which is very injurious to the teeth, or destroying works of art, which are hidden away in public galleries and seldom seen. I told my friends of my theory, which they warmly applauded, and between us we soon devised our plan.

In two days' time would take place at Lord's the famous match, Gentlemen and Players—though, as Agatha said, what irony in the title! Gentlemen! The creatures who arrested and bullied women. Players! men who had refused fair play to the gentler sex. But setting that aside, our plan was as follows. Lately the weather had been very uncertain, demanding, as I knew from watching cricket matches with my family, the curious, bulky protectors from rain, which they sometimes put over the pitch at night. If this weather continued, Agatha and I would contrive to stay in the grounds the day before, and to hide underneath these things till they were removed just before the match started, and then—well, our hearts would tell us how to act.

All went well. As luck would have it, the weather was so uncertain, that the tarpaulins were not removed until I could tell by the clapping that the umpires were just coming out to the wickets. Then the covers were slowly wheeled away, disclosing Agatha's and my recumbent forms, lying one at each wicket. What a shock for the men!

Never shall I forget the next few minutes. We sprang up and unfurled our flags, crying ' Votes for Women ' and marching up and down the pitch, while police and groundsmen appeared from all sides and the crowd shouted and waved their arms like lunatics. We were now determined to be arrested, and to that end I slapped the constable, who seized me, in the face. But to my exasperation he only smiled. I kicked his shins. He dared to laugh. I bit him—he had the effrontery to say it tickled. Finally I was driven to do what I hoped to avoid, because I knew how deeply grieved Addle would be when he read of it in the papers. In my pocket was a small bottle of water, and I now managed to get it out, extract the cork and to pour the contents *on to the wicket*. At once a howl of execration went up from the entire ground. Agatha, seeing the effect of my action, did the same. At last the faces of the policemen changed from maddening good-humour to stern disapproval, and we were placed under arrest and marched off the ground.

Actually, I was only twenty-four hours in prison. Then the Governor himself appeared and told me I was free. In answer to my indignant inquiry as to the cause of my release, he mumbled something about a cable from Norway and having been at Eton with Addle. I was furious with my husband for daring to interfere and refused to see him the next week. Instead Emily Coop and I did all we could for Agatha by marching up and down outside the prison walls, and singing our own particular song, which we had composed to the tune of ' Three Fishers '—' For men must learn that women must vote.' After three weeks she was discharged, having put up a splendid fight by breaking her cell window and hitting her wardress with a toothbrush.

It was wonderful to be united again, yet somehow the old charm had vanished. Perhaps it was a fore-taste of the end ; perhaps it was due to the strained relations that, I regret to say, existed between my husband and myself at this time. When he wrote : ' Come home ; I miss you ', I wrote back : ' Not as much as we miss the vote.' He telegraphed : ' I demand that you return ' ; I wired back : ' We demand equal rights.' It was Agatha who encouraged this policy, worded the messages, pressed me to stay away from Addle, until he came whole-heartedly into the fight with us. And Agatha seemed my dearest friend.

It is painful to me to write of this time, but I am determined to conceal nothing from the public, even to save myself from criticism. It is quite true that for a time I did feel it my duty to support the cause and my friendship with Agatha by refusing to go home ; and we actually started to make plans for the future together. Then came my terrible disillusionment.

It started by Agatha suggesting that we should leave the flat because it was too luxurious, and live in Ber-mondsey instead, devoting our lives to the suffrage cause in the slums. That I did not mind—my dear mother had always approved of slumming. But to say that the Pimlico flat was *too luxurious* ! When I had slept for weeks in a room no bigger than a cupboard and dressed in acute discomfort. I could not help saying this and contrasting it with what I had been used to, when to my astonishment and horror Agatha burst out into a tirade against wealth and position saying that I had no right to enjoy such privileges, and that noble birth was a stigma to be lived down only by hardship. Then suddenly the dreadful truth, to which I had been blind all these years, swept over me. Addle had been right in advising me against her friendship. I had been mistaken, unless, indeed, she had altered. But whatever she had been in the past, there was no doubt about it now. *Agatha Slubb-Repp was a Socialist !*

I took the next train back to Bengers and was greeted by my dear husband, who immediately forgave all. That same evening I sat facing him across the dazzling white damask tablecloth, laden with priceless McClutch silver, enjoying the dinner he had ordered of all the most exquisite dishes, together with a bottle of Chateau Yquem—after orangeade my favourite drink—and I thought how blessed was home life and how sacred its privileges.

Another little song I wrote for the cause. I am inclined to regard this as the best literary work I have done.

> There's a mission in our lives,
>   There's a beacon flare,
> Lighting every woman's heart—
>   Let them scoff who dare !
> If our bonnet holds a bee,
> It can sting, as men will see.
>
> Votes for Women—is our cry.
>   Let us blaze the trail.
> Ours to win the vote, or die
>   Badgering the male.
> We've the bravery of Fox,
>   The eloquence of Chatham.
> Shall we be deterred by frocks ?
>   Up, girls, and at 'em !
>
> Mothers, teach your lisping babes
>   What the franchise means.
> Schoolgirls, learn of suffrage joys
>   Ere you reach your 'teens.
> Each in her small way may plan
> Inconvenience to some man.

AN ANTHEM

Votes for Women—is our cry.
   Hear our Leader's call.
Ours is not to reason why
   Nor to think at all.
Ours is but to blindly strike
   'Gainst a man-made system.
Let's not be too ladylike !
   Up, girls, and fist 'em.

Time will come and that right soon
   When the world will grant
Woman's rights, and we shall have
   Everything we want.
Then we must not fail or faint.
We will find a new complaint.

Votes for Women—is our cry.
   Boldly we will strive,
While any man would pass us by
   And dare remain alive.
Do they still regard our sex
   As a minor item ?
Sound the trumpet, clear the decks !
   Up, girls, and bite 'em !

CHAPTER XII

MY TREASURES

Flowers are lovely ; love is flower-like ;
    Friendship is a sheltering tree ;
Oh, the joys that come down shower-like,
    Of friendships, love, and liberty.
                Coleridge : 'Youth and Age.'

I AM ending my story with the happenings described in the last chapter, not because my life since that date has been empty of incident, for it has been a full and happy one, but because I always look back on that time as the last of a somewhat adventurous and dramatic girlhood and the beginning of a serene matronhood. It is as though the little bark, tossed on the waters of Fate for so long, had come to port at last and was safely moored there, unloading its treasures. And the treasures which I have been privileged to have aboard have been many and precious.

First of all, my children—James, who grew from a braw wee laddie into a bonnie man—I never can resist the dear old Scottish idioms—and is now, having retired from his father's regiment after the Great War, working hard on the Stock Exchange—so hard, in fact, that he fears he will have to give up his third day's hunting in the week, which is a great privation ; but I have taught my sons that duty comes before everything, and it is good to know that they have learnt their lesson. Hector, the second, is a splendid boy, too. Unfortunately, he failed for the army, the law, and the civil service, and did not take to business. But all's well that ends well, and we are proud to say that he has just been successful in his third by-election and is now an M.P. It is also delightful for us, as he is able to be at home constantly, both at Bengers and in Scotland. Last, but by no means least, there is our dear Margaret, born in 1912, and the last symbol, it often seems to me, of happy peace-time life, before the calamity of the war broke upon us.

I am not going to write much of that terrible time, except to say that I am proud to think that all my family did their bit. Addle, of course, at once offered his services to his country, and was found so valuable as a trainer of men that he was kept in England all the time. I did what I could in several directions, and myself inaugurated a little band of women, who devoted themselves solely to knitting silk body-bands for the Staff, for I found out from several of my family, including Crainy, who were on it, that staff officers, with their long enforced periods of idleness, were far more susceptible to chills than men in the busier trench life. Mipsie, of course, as everyone will remember, ran a famous and successful canteen which came to an unhappy end, following on some silly rumour that a well-known general had been found there one night dancing the one-step, clad entirely in rose-leaves. All the men adored her and always lovingly referred to the house (which was officially known as the Brisket Canteen, as Mipsie, in between her husbands, always returned to her original married name) as ' The Juicy Joint ' and, this I believe, was the origin of the American slang expression now used in cinematograph films I am told.

Humpo also did well. He was too old to join up, but, with all the pluck of a Coot, volunteered as a stoker, which at the age of forty-three was, I think, really magnificent of him. He was responsible for the fires of a whole floor in the Home Office, and became such an expert in the putting on of coal, that the rooms he looked after achieved the reputation of being the warmest and most comfortable in Whitehall, which is high praise indeed. He was justly rewarded with the O.B.E. for his splendid work.

Perhaps this would be a good moment to speak of his marriage, which took place soon after my own, when he was twenty-four, to Miss Rosie Scrunch. People have been very malicious about his wife, spreading it about that she was a barmaid, which is emphatically a lie. Though it is quite true that she was working in that part of the Empire Theatre where the bar was when Humpo met her, her work was confined to super-intending the other girls, and only occasionally min-istering to a client's wants by the distribution of a sandwich or a cake—surely a womanly occupation, if not altogether socially irreproachable. She was considerably older than my brother and I cannot pretend that the marriage was not something of a disappointment to my father, though beyond cutting Humpo out of his will he never showed it ; but Rosie has been a good wife and mother, and their only son, Ernie, has had quite a success on the stage, where he has made a name for himself as the butler in many well-known plays.

To return to my own family, Margaret, who is now twenty-four, is a dear girl, and a great comfort and help in the home. She is rather fuller in the figure than seems to be the fashion nowadays for girls, and has a somewhat florid complexion ; but she has a natural charm all her own, which perhaps I am the only one to see. She is very shy—she takes after Crainy in that—and does not make friends easily, especially among young men, but I am sure that to some man who had the good sense to look beyond mere superficial prettiness for solid worth in his mate, Margaret would make an admirable wife, and my heart is set on seeing her settled with a really good husband— of suitable social and financial standing, of course. Indeed, all my life is now directed to this sacred object. I have tackled difficult—nay, wellnigh impossible things before, but never with such determination as I face this, perhaps the last great struggle of my career.

Other treasures in life are so numerous, that it is hard to pick them out. Music, dancing, and the gift of friendship, books—which surely are friends too—the song of birds, a garden ! 'A garden is a lovesome thing, God wot,' is carved by the estate carpenter just under the coronet on all our garden seats. I am very fond of quotations and mottoes, and always take great pleasure in thinking out suitable ones. 'Sermons in stones' I have picked out in white pebbles in my rock garden ; on my jewel case, which contains some very valuable and beautiful heirlooms, is stamped : 'Base envy withers at another's joy', and round the silver coasters which hold our priceless port, I have had engraved 'A little goes a long way ' and ' Enough is as good as a feast ', just as a playful warning to the gentlemen after the restraint of feminine influence is removed. But my most apt quotation was in a little pamphlet I wrote on the cruelty of docking puppies' tails : ' There's a divinity which shapes our ends,' which I thought rather neat, I must say. It was a campaign I supported vigorously for some time, until, in fact, my attention and energy were suddenly diverted to a new scandal, the grave immorality for which men and women of high station and conduct are responsible by not keeping their cats under proper control at nighttime. It was a subject on which I felt very deeply and was proud to work for.

Work ! What would life be without it ? The great pleasure and interest derived from doing all one can to improve and influence other people's lives by giving generously of that wisdom and instinct for guidance which is the natural inheritance of the aristocracy. I have been able, I rejoice to think, to help several splendid causes by acting as President and sometimes even Vice-president, notably, besides others I have mentioned in earlier chapters, the honourable Society of Dames Errant, the Guild of Gladdery, the Anti-lipstick League, the Society for the Preservation of Ancient Bishops, the Barley Water Union, and the Home Truth League, the last a splendidly plucky little society, which is unfortunately rather under the weather just now, owing to a serious schism in the committee. These are apart from such local activities as the Institute and the Mothers' Union, of which I think I may say they literally could not get on without me, and various county organizations, which I am only too glad to lead, like the Hertfordshire Hikers' Hose Guild—we supply free stockings to hundreds of poor business girls, who evidently cannot afford them and disgrace the countryside by their bare legs—and our County Children's Rabbit Club, an excellent way of encouraging the children to feed and preserve wild rabbits, of which Addle for some unknown reason disapproves, but I am quite undaunted by that and am delighted to show my official approval by becoming Great White Mother Bunny.

And so life goes on, with its high lights and its shadows, for that is how its joys and sorrows always appear to the artist in me. I have had my full share of both, and I have not attempted in my autobiography to conceal the dark places in my life ; rather have I tried to illuminate them by the clear, piercing light of honesty and truth, for the sake of my many friends, both known and unknown to me, who will read these pages and will say : ' That is how a British Aristocrat behaves in face of sorrow, and hardship, and danger.'

Yet on re-reading what I have written, I am conscious of a certain misgiving—Have I said too much ?   For in my impulsive desire to set out the whole truth and stand right with the world and with my own conscience, in my earnest endeavour to help others, especially other women, by the experience of a woman, no better than themselves, except perhaps in birth, I know that I have been fearlessly frank. . . .   Perhaps too frank ?

ENVOI

Let wealth and commerce, law and learning die,
But leave us still our old nobility.—

> *John James Robert Manners,*
> *Duke of Rutland :*
> *' England's Trust.'*